YEAR 1

Patterns

Dan Fendel and Diane Resek
with
Lynne Alper and Sherry Fraser

KEY CURRICULUM PRESS
Innovators in Mathematics Education

This material is based upon work supported by the National Science Foundation under award number ESI-9255262. Any opinions, findings, and conclusions or recommendations expressed in this publication are those of the authors and do not necessarily reflect the views of the National Science Foundation.

Key Curriculum Press
P.O. Box 2304
Berkeley, California 94702
editorial@keypress.com
http://www.keypress.com

10 9 8 7 6 5 4 3 00 99 98 97
ISBN 1-55953-251-3
Printed in the
United States of America

Project Editor
Casey FitzSimons

Additional Editorial Development
Dan Bennett, Bill Finzer, Crystal Mills

Editorial Production
Caroline Ayres, Debbie Cogan,
Greer Lleuad, Jason Luz

Editorial Assistants
Jeff Gammon, Romy Snyder

Teacher Reviews
Dave Calhoun, John Chart, Dwight Fuller,
Donna Gaarder, Dan Johnson, Jean Klanica,
Cathie Thompson

Multicultural Reviews
Edward Castillo, Ph.D., Sonoma State University
Genevieve Lau, Ph.D., Skyline College

Cover and Interior Design
Terry Lockman
Lumina Designworks

Cover Photography and Cover Illustration
Hillary Turner and Tom Fowler

Production
Luis Shein

Production Coordination
Susan Parini

Technical Graphics
Greg Reeves

Illustration
Tom Fowler, Evangelia Philippidis,
Diane Varner, Martha Weston,
April Goodman Willy

Publisher
Steven Rasmussen

Editorial Director
John Bergez

Acknowledgments

Many people have contributed to the development of the IMP curriculum, including the hundreds of teachers and many thousands of students who used preliminary versions of the materials. Of course, there is no way to thank all of them individually, but the IMP directors want to give some special acknowledgments.

We want to give extraordinary thanks to the following people who played unique roles in the development of the curriculum.

- **Bill Finzer** was one of the original directors of IMP before going on to different pastures. He helped shape the overall vision of the program, and worked on drafts of several Year 1 units.
- **Matt Bremer** did the initial revision of every unit after its pilot testing. Each unit of the curriculum also underwent extensive focus group reexamination after being taught for several years, and Matt did the rewrite of many units following the focus groups. He has read every word of everyone else's revisions as well, and has contributed tremendous insight through his understanding of high school students and the high school classroom.
- **Mary Jo Cittadino** became a high school student once again during the piloting of the curriculum, attending class daily and doing all the class activities, homework, and POWs. Because of this experience, her contributions to focus groups had a unique perspective. This is a good place to thank her also for her contributions to IMP as Network Coordinator for California. In that capacity, she has visited many IMP classrooms and answered thousands of questions from parents, teachers, and administrators.
- **Lori Green** left the classroom as a regular teacher after the 1989-90 school year and became a traveling resource for IMP classroom teachers. In that role, she has seen more classes using the curriculum than we can count, and the insights from her classroom observations have been a valuable resource in her work in the focus groups.
- **Celia Stevenson** developed the charming and witty graphics that graced the pre-publication versions of all the IMP units.

Several people played particular roles in the development of this unit, *Patterns:*

- Matt Bremer, Janice Bussey, Donna Gaarder, Lori Green, and Tom Zimmerman helped us create the version of *Patterns* that was pilot tested during 1989-90. They not only taught the unit in their classrooms that year, but also read and commented on early drafts, tested out almost all the activities during workshops that preceded the teaching, and then came back after teaching the unit with insights that contributed to the initial revision.

- Dean Ballard, Greg Smith, and Barbara Schallau joined Matt Bremer, Mary Jo Cittadino, and Lori Green for the focus group on *Patterns* in May, 1993. Their contributions were built on several years of IMP teaching, including at least two years teaching this unit, and their work led to the development of the last field-test version of the unit.
- Dan Branham, Dave Calhoun, John Chart, Steve Hansen, Mary Hunter, Caran Resciniti, Gwennyth Trice, and Julie Walker field tested the post-focus-group version of *Patterns* during 1994-95. Dave and John met with us when the teaching of the unit was finished to share their experiences. Their feedback helped shape the final version that now appears.

In creating this program, we needed help in many dimensions other than writing curriculum and giving support to teachers.

The National Science Foundation has been the primary sponsor of the Interactive Mathematics Program. We want to thank NSF for its ongoing support, and especially want to extend our personal thanks to Dr. Margaret Cozzens, Director of NSF's Division of Elementary, Secondary, and Informal Education, for her encouragement and her faith in our efforts.

We also want to acknowledge here the initial support for curriculum development from the California Postsecondary Education Commission and the San Francisco Foundation, and the major support for dissemination from the Noyce Foundation and the David and Lucile Packard Foundation.

Keeping all of our work going required the help of a first-rate office staff. This group of talented and hard-working individuals worked tirelessly on many tasks, such as sending out units, keeping the books balanced, helping us get our message out to the public, and handling communications with schools, teachers, and administrators. We greatly appreciate their dedication.

- Barbara Ford—Secretary
- Tony Gillies—Project Manager
- Marianne Smith—Publicist
- Linda Witnov—Outreach Coordinator

We want to thank Dr. Norman Webb, of the Wisconsin Center for Education Research, for his leadership in our evaluation program, and our Evaluation Advisory Board, whose expertise was so valuable in that aspect of our work.

- David Clarke, University of Melbourne
- Robert Davis, Rutgers University
- George Hein, Lesley College
- Mark St. John, Inverness Research Associates

IMP National Advisory Board

We have been further supported in this work by our National Advisory Board—a group of very busy people who found time in their schedules to give us more than a piece of their minds every year. We thank them for their ideas and their forthrightness.

David Blackwell
Professor of Mathematics and Statistics
University of California, Berkeley

Constance Clayton
Professor of Pediatrics
Chief, Division of Community Health Care
Medical College of Pennsylvania

Tom Ferrio
Manager, Professional Calculators
Texas Instruments

Andrew M. Gleason
Hollis Professor of Mathematics and Natural Philosophy
Department of Mathematics
Harvard University

Milton Gordon
President and Professor of Mathematics
California State University, Fullerton

Shirley Hill
Curator's Professor of Education and Mathematics
School of Education
University of Missouri

Steven Leinwand
Mathematics Consultant
Connecticut Department of Education

Art McArdle
Northern California Surveyors Apprentice Committee

Diane Ravitch (1994 only)
Brookings Institution

Roy Romer (1992-1994 only)
Governor
State of Colorado

Karen Sheingold
Research Director
Educational Testing Service

Theodore R. Sizer
Chairman
Coalition of Essential Schools

Gary D. Watts
Educational Consultant

Finally, we want to thank Steve Rasmussen, President of Key Curriculum Press, Casey FitzSimons, Key's Project Editor for the IMP curriculum, and the many others at Key whose work turned our ideas and words into published form.

Dan Fendel Diane Resek Lynne Alper Sherry Fraser

The Interactive Mathematics Program

What is the Interactive Mathematics Program?

The Interactive Mathematics Program (IMP) is a growing collaboration of mathematicians, teacher-educators, and teachers who have been working together since 1989 on both curriculum development and teacher professional development.

What is the IMP curriculum?

IMP has created a four-year program of problem-based mathematics that replaces the traditional Algebra I–Geometry–Algebra II/Trigonometry–Precalculus sequence and that is designed to exemplify the curriculum reform called for in the *Curriculum and Evaluation Standards* of the National Council of Teachers of Mathematics.

The IMP curriculum integrates traditional material with additional topics recommended by the NCTM *Standards*, such as statistics, probability, curve fitting, and matrix algebra. Although every IMP unit has a specific mathematical focus (for instance, similar triangles), most units are structured around a central problem and bring in other topics as needed to solve that problem, rather than narrowly restricting the mathematical content. Ideas that are developed in one unit are generally revisited and deepened in one or more later units.

For which students is the IMP curriculum intended?

The IMP curriculum is for all students. One of IMP's goals is to make the learning of a core mathematics curriculum accessible to everyone. Toward that end, we have designed the program for use with heterogeneous classes. We provide you with a varied collection of supplemental problems to give you the flexibility to meet individual student needs.

Teacher Phyllis Quick confers with a group of students.

How is the IMP classroom different?

When you use the IMP curriculum, your role changes from "imparter of knowledge" to observer and facilitator. You ask challenging questions. You do not give all the answers but you prod students to do their own thinking, to make generalizations, and to go beyond the immediate problem by asking themselves "What if?"

The IMP curriculum gives students many opportunities to write about their mathematical thinking, to reflect on what they have done, and to make oral presentations to each other about their work. In IMP, your assessment of students becomes integrated with learning, and you evaluate students in a variety of ways, including class participation, daily homework assignments, Problems of the Week, portfolios, and unit assessments. The IMP *Teaching Handbook* provides many practical suggestions for teachers on how to get the best possible results using this curriculum in *your* classroom.

What is in Year 1 of the IMP curriculum?

Year 1 of the IMP curriculum contains five units.

Patterns

The primary purpose of this unit is to introduce students to ways of working on and thinking about mathematics that may be new to them. In a sense, the unit is an overall introduction to the IMP curriculum, which involves changes for many students in how they learn mathematics and what they think of as mathematics. The main mathematical ideas of the unit include function tables, the use of variables, positive and negative numbers, and some basic geometrical concepts.

The Game of Pig

A dice game called Pig forms the core of this unit. Playing and analyzing Pig involves students in a wide variety of mathematical activities. The basic problem for students is to find an optimum strategy for playing the game. In order to find a good strategy and prove that it is optimum, students work with the concept of expected value and develop a mathematical analysis for the game based on an area model for probability.

The Overland Trail

This unit looks at the mid-nineteenth century western migration across what is now the United States in terms of the many mathematical relationships involved. These relationships involve planning what to take on the 2400-mile trek, estimating the cost of the move, studying rates of consumption and of travel, and estimating the time to reach the final goal. A major mathematical focus of the unit is the use of equations, tables, and graphs to describe real-life situations.

The Pit and the Pendulum

In Edgar Allan Poe's story, *The Pit and the Pendulum,* a prisoner is tied down while a pendulum with a sharp blade slowly descends. If the prisoner does not act, he will be killed by the pendulum. Students read an excerpt from the story, and are presented with the problem of whether the prisoner would have enough time to escape. To resolve this question, they construct pendulums and conduct experiments. In the process, they are introduced to the concepts of normal distribution and standard deviation as tools for determining whether a change in one variable really does affect another. They use graphing calculators to learn about quadratic equations and to explore curve fitting. Finally, after deriving a theoretical answer to the pendulum problem, students actually build a thirty-foot pendulum to test their theory.

Shadows

The central question of this unit is, "How can you predict the length of a shadow?" The unit moves quickly from this concrete problem to the geometric concept of similarity. Students work with a variety of approaches to come to an understanding of similar polygons, especially similar triangles. Then they return to the problem of the shadow, applying their knowledge of similar triangles and using informal methods for solving proportions, to develop a general formula. In the last part of the unit, students learn about the three primary trigonometric functions—sine, cosine, and tangent—as they apply to acute angles, and they apply these functions to problems of finding heights and distances.

How do the four years of the IMP curriculum fit together?

The four years of the IMP curriculum form an integrated sequence through which students can learn the mathematics they will need, both for further education and on the job. Although the organization of the IMP curriculum is very different from the traditional Algebra I–Geometry–Algebra II/Trigonometry–Precalculus sequence, the important mathematical ideas are all there.

Here are some examples of how both traditional concepts and topics new to the high school curriculum are developed.

Linear equations

In Year 1 of the IMP curriculum, students develop an intuitive foundation about algebraic thinking, including the use of variables, which they build on throughout the program. In the Year 2 unit *Solve It!,* students use the concept of equivalent equations to see how to solve any linear equation in a single variable. Later in Year 2, in a unit called *Cookies* (about maximizing profits for a bakery), they solve pairs of linear equations in two variables, using both algebraic and geometric methods. In the Year 3 unit *Meadows or Malls?,* they extend those ideas to systems with more than two variables, and see how to use matrices and the technology of graphing calculators to solve such systems.

Measurement and the Pythagorean theorem

Measurement, including area and volume, is one of the fundamental topics in geometry. The Pythagorean theorem is one of the most important geometric principles ever discovered. In the Year 2 unit *Do Bees Build It Best?,* students combine these ideas with their knowledge of similarity (from the Year 1 unit *Shadows*) to see why the hexagonal prism of the bees' honeycomb design is the most efficient regular prism possible. Students also use the Pythagorean theorem in later units, applying it to develop principles like the distance formula in coordinate geometry.

Trigonometric functions

In traditional programs, the trigonometric functions are introduced in the eleventh or twelfth grade. In the IMP curriculum, students begin working with trigonometry in Year 1 (in *Shadows*), using right-triangle trigonometry in several units (including *Do Bees Build It Best?*) in Years 2 and 3. In the Year 4 unit *High Dive,* they extend trigonometry from right triangles to circular functions, in the context of a circus act in which a performer falls from a Ferris wheel into a moving tub of water. (In *High Dive,* students also learn principles of physics, developing laws for falling objects and finding the vertical and horizontal components of velocity.)

Standard deviation and the binomial distribution

Standard deviation and the binomial distribution are major tools in the study of probability and statistics. *The Game of Pig* gets students started by building a firm understanding of concepts of probability and the phenomenon of experimental variation. Later in Year 1 (in *The Pit and the Pendulum*), they use standard deviation to see that the period of a pendulum is determined primarily by its length. In Year 2, they compare standard deviation with the chi-square test in examining whether a set of data is statistically significant. In *Pennant Fever* (Year 3), students use the binomial distribution to evaluate a team's chances of winning the baseball championship, and in *The Pollster's Dilemma* (Year 4), students tie many of these ideas together in the central limit theorem, seeing how the margin of error and the level of certainty for an election poll depend on its size.

Does the program work?

The IMP curriculum has been thoroughly field-tested by hundreds of classroom teachers around the country. Their enthusiasm comes from the success they have seen in their own classrooms with their own students. For those who measure success by test scores, we mention that repeated studies have proved that IMP students do at least as well as students in traditional mathematics classes on tests like the SAT, even though IMP students spend far less time than traditional students on the algebra and geometry skills emphasized by these tests. With the time saved, IMP students learn topics such as statistics that other students don't see until they reach college.

But one of our proudest achievements is that IMP students are excited about mathematics, as shown by the fact that they take more mathematics courses in high school than their counterparts in traditional programs. We think this is because they see that mathematics can be relevant to their own lives. If so, then the program works.

Dan Fendel
Diane Resek
Lynne Alper
Sherry Fraser

Welcome!

Note to Students

These pages in the student book welcome students to the program.

You are about to begin an adventure in mathematics, an adventure organized around interesting, complex problems. The concepts you learn grow out of what is needed to solve those problems.

This curriculum was developed by the Interactive Mathematics Program (IMP), a collaboration of teachers, teacher-educators, and mathematicians who have been working together since 1989 to reform the way high school mathematics is taught. About one hundred thousand students and five hundred teachers used these materials before they were published. Their experiences, reactions, and ideas have been incorporated into the final version you now hold.

Our goal is to give you the mathematics you need to succeed in this changing world. We want to present mathematics to you in a manner that reflects how mathematics is used and reflects the different ways people work and learn together. Through this perspective on mathematics, you will be prepared both for continued study of mathematics in college and for the world of work.

This book contains the various assignments that will be your work during Year 1 of the program. As you will see, these assignments incorporate ideas from many branches of mathematics, including algebra, geometry, probability, graphing, statistics, and trigonometry. Other topics will come up in later parts of this four-year program. Rather than present each of these areas separately, we have integrated them and presented them in meaningful contexts so that you'll see how they relate to one another and to our world.

Each unit in this four-year program has a central problem or theme, and focuses on several major mathematical ideas. Within each unit, the material is organized for teaching purposes into "Days," with a homework assignment for each day. (Your class may not follow this schedule exactly, especially if it doesn't meet every day.)

At the end of the main material for each unit, you will find a set of "supplemental problems." These problems provide additional opportunities for you to work with ideas from the unit, either to strengthen your understanding of the core material or to explore new ideas related to the unit.

Although the IMP program is not organized into courses called Algebra, Geometry, and so on, you will be learning all the essential mathematical concepts that are part of those traditional courses. You will also be learning concepts from branches of mathematics—especially statistics and probability—that are not part of a traditional high school program.

To accomplish this goal, you will have to be an active learner. Simply reading this book will not allow you to achieve your goal, because the book does not teach directly. Your role as a mathematics student will be to experiment, investigate, ask questions, make and test conjectures, and reflect, and then communicate your ideas and conclusions both verbally and in writing. You will do some work in collaboration with your fellow students, just as users of mathematics in the real world often work in teams. At other times, you will be working on your own.

We hope you will enjoy the challenge of this new way of learning mathematics and will see mathematics in a new light.

Dan Fendel Diane Resek Lynne Alper Sherry Fraser

Finding What You Need

We designed this guide to help you find what you need amid all the information it provides. Each of the following components has a special treatment in the layout of the guide.

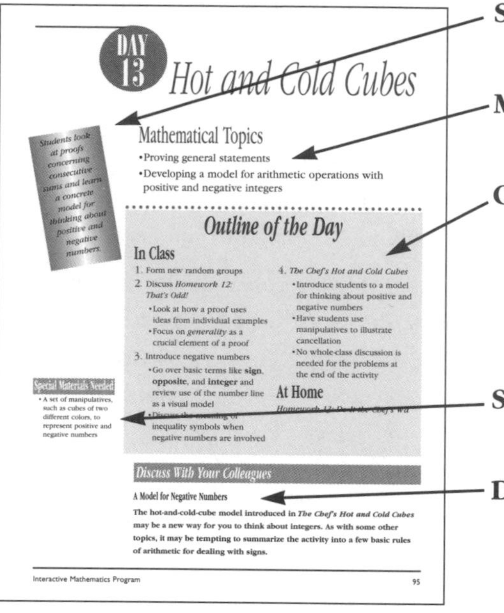

DAY 13 Hot and Cold Cubes

Students look at proofs concerning consecutive sums and learn a concrete model for thinking about positive and negative numbers.

Mathematical Topics

- Proving general statements
- Developing a model for arithmetic operations with positive and negative integers

Outline of the Day

In Class

1. Form new random groups
2. Discuss *Homework 12: That's Odd!*
   - Look at how a proof uses ideas from individual examples
   - Focus on *generality* as a crucial element of a proof
3. Introduce negative numbers
   - Go over basic terms like **sign**, **opposite**, and **integer** and review use of the number line as a visual model
   - inequality symbols when negative numbers are involved
4. *The Chef's Hot and Cold Cubes*
   - Introduce students to a model for thinking about positive and negative numbers
   - Have students use manipulatives to illustrate cancellation
   - No whole-class discussion is needed for the problems at the end of the activity

At Home

Special Materials Needed

- A set of manipulatives, such as cubes of two different colors, to represent positive and negative numbers

Discuss With Your Colleagues

A Model for Negative Numbers

The hot-and-cold-cube model introduced in *The Chef's Hot and Cold Cubes* may be a new way for you to think about integers. As with some other topics, it may be tempting to summarize the activity into a few basic rules of arithmetic for dealing with signs.

Interactive Mathematics Program 95

Synopsis of the Day: The key idea or activity for each day is summarized in a brief sentence or two.

Mathematical Topics: Mathematical issues for the day are presented in a bulleted list.

Outline of the Day: Under the *In Class* heading, the outline summarizes the activities for the day, which are keyed to numbered headings in the discussion. Daily homework assignments and Problems of the Week are listed under the *At Home* heading.

Special Materials Needed: Special items needed in the classroom for each day are bulleted here.

Discuss With Your Colleagues: This section highlights topics that you may want to discuss with your peers.

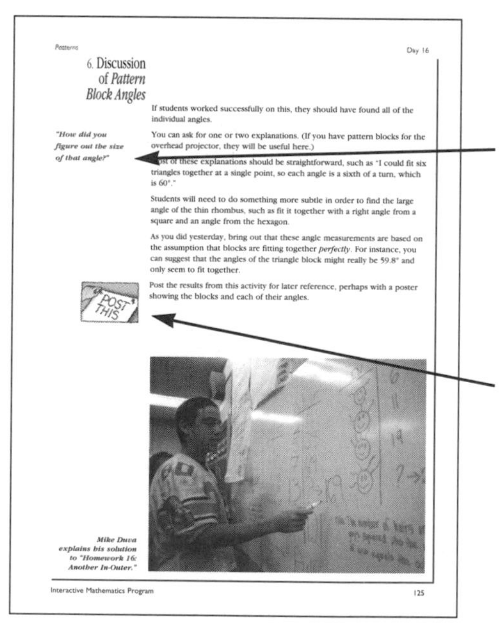

Patterns Day 16

6. Discussion of *Pattern Block Angles*

If students worked successfully on this, they should have found all of the individual angles.

"How did you figure out the size of that angle?"

You can ask for one or two explanations. (If you have pattern blocks for the overhead projector, they will be useful here.)

of these explanations should be straightforward, such as "I could fit six triangles together at a single point, so each angle is a sixth of a turn, which is 60°."

Students will need to do something more subtle in order to find the large angle of the thin rhombus, such as fit it together with a right angle from a square and an angle from the hexagon.

As you did yesterday, bring out that these angle measurements are based on the assumption that blocks are fitting together *perfectly*. For instance, you can suggest that the angles of the triangle block might really be 59.8° and only seem to fit together.

POST THIS

Post the results from this activity for later reference, perhaps with a poster showing the blocks and each of their angles.

Mike Duva explains his solution to "Homework 16: Another In-Outer."

Interactive Mathematics Program 125

Suggested Questions: These are specific questions that you might ask during an activity or discussion to promote student insight or to determine whether students understand an idea. The appropriateness of these questions generally depends on what students have already developed or presented on their own.

Post This: The *Post This* icon indicates items that you may want to display in the classroom.

Icons for Student Written Products

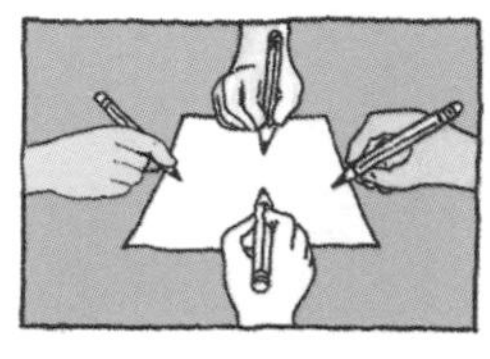

Single Group report

Individual reports

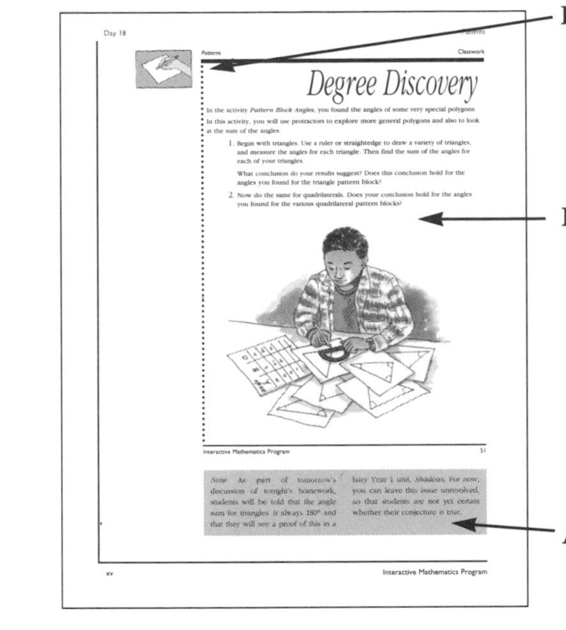

Day 18

Patterns | Classwork

Degree Discovery

In the activity *Pattern Block Angles*, you found the angles of some very special polygons. In this activity, you will use protractors to explore more general polygons and also to look at the sum of the angles.

1. Begin with triangles. Use a ruler or straightedge to draw a variety of triangles, and measure the angles for each triangle. Then find the sum of the angles for each of your triangles.

   What conclusion do your results suggest? Does this conclusion hold for the angles you found for the triangle pattern block?

2. Now do the same for quadrilaterals. Does your conclusion hold for the angles you found for the various quadrilateral pattern blocks?

Interactive Mathematics Program 51

Note: As part of tomorrow's discussion of tonight's homework, students will be told that the angle sum for triangles *is* always 180° and that they will see a proof of this in a later Year 1 unit, *Shadows*. For now, you can leave this issue unresolved, so that students are not yet certain whether their conjecture is true.

xv Interactive Mathematics Program

Icons for Student Written Products: For each group activity, there is an icon suggesting a single group report, individual reports, or no report at all. If graphs are included, the icon indicates this as well. (The graph icons do not appear in *Patterns*.)

Embedded Student Pages: Embedded within the pages of the teacher guide are reduced-size copies of the pages from the student book. These reduced student pages include the "transition pages" that appear occasionally within each unit to summarize each portion of the unit and to prepare students for what is coming. Having all of these student pages in the teacher guide is a helpful way for you to see things from the students' perspective.

Asides: These are ideas outside the main thrust of a discussion. They include background information for teachers, refinements or subtle points that may only be of interest to some students, ways to help fill in gaps in understanding the main ideas, and suggestions about when to bring in a particular concept.

Additional Information

Here is a brief outline of other tools we have included to assist you and make both the teaching and the learning experience more rewarding.

Glossary: This section, which is found at the back of the book, gives the definitions of important terms for all of Year 1 for easy reference. The same glossary appears in the student book.

Appendix A: Supplemental Problems: This appendix contains a variety of interesting additional activities for the unit, for teachers who would like to supplement material found in the regular classroom problems. These additional activities are of two types—*reinforcements,* which help increase student understanding of concepts that are central to the unit, and *extensions,* which allow students to explore ideas beyond the basic unit.

Appendix B: Blackline Masters: For each unit, this appendix contains materials you can reproduce that are not available in the student book and that will be helpful to teacher and student alike. They include the end-of-unit assessments as well as such items as diagrams from which you can make transparencies. Semester assessments for Year 1 are included in *The Overland Trail* (for first semester) and *Shadows* (for second semester).

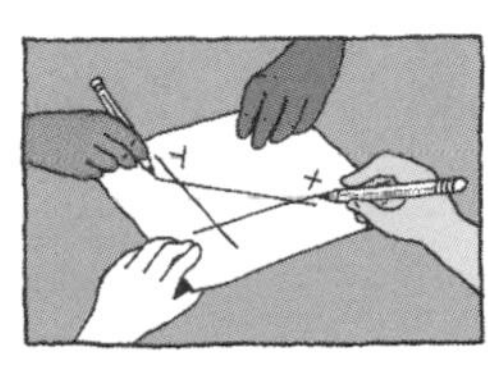

Single group graph

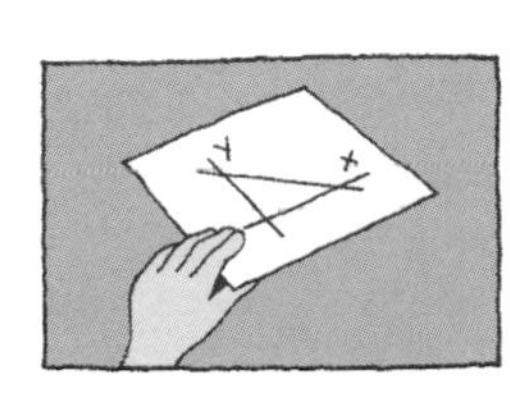

Individual graphs

No report at all

"Patterns" Overview

Summary of the Unit

The primary purpose of this unit is to introduce students to ways of working on and thinking about mathematics that may be new to them. The unit is a general introduction to the Interactive Mathematics Program (IMP), which entails changes for many students in how they learn mathematics and in what they regard as mathematics. A major emphasis of the unit is on developing the ability to think about and explore mathematical problems.

Some of the important mathematical ideas and concepts introduced in *Patterns* are In-Out tables, the use of variables, positive and negative numbers, and basic geometrical concepts.

The concept of proof is another major theme of the unit. Proof is not developed as a formal process, but rather as part of the larger theme of reasoning and explaining. Students' ability to create and understand proofs will develop over the course of the four-year IMP curriculum, and their work in this unit is just a start.

The outline below gives a summary of the unit's overall organization and of some of the main activities.

- Days 1-4: Introduction to IMP, to the unit, to calculators, and to the Problem of the Week (POW) write-up
- Days 5-6: Introduction to In-Out machines
- Day 7: *Marcella's Bagels* and more about write-ups
- Day 8: *Lonesome Llama,* an activity that focuses on the process of working collaboratively
- Day 9: Presentations of *POW 1: The Broken Eggs* and order-of-operations rules
- Days 10-12: *Consecutive Sums,* an open-ended group investigation
- Days 13-14: Introduction of negative numbers
- Day 15: Presentations of *POW 2: 1-2-3-4 Puzzle* and introduction of pattern blocks
- Days 16-19: Introduction to angles, the use of protractors, and the study of angle sums for polygons
- Days 20-21: Sharing of write-ups and discussion of *POW 3: Checkerboard Squares*

- Days 22–23: Programming calculators to behave like In-Out machines
- Days 24–26: Portfolios, end-of-unit assessments, and summing up

The IMP *Teaching Handbook* contains some guidelines about varying from the day-by-day schedule set up in this guide.

Concepts and Skills

This unit introduces some general learning skills and methods that will be used and developed throughout the four-year IMP curriculum. These include

- working in groups to analyze problems
- learning about group cooperation and roles in group learning
- expressing mathematical ideas orally and in writing
- making presentations within small groups and to the whole class
- developing strategies for solving problems
- using concrete mathematical models in various situations
- doing investigations where the task is not clearly defined
- becoming familiar with alternative forms of assessment, such as self-assessment and portfolios
- learning about the use of a graphing calculator, including programming

This unit also includes specific mathematical content. In the course of this unit, students will

- analyze and create In-Out tables
- use variables to express generalizations
- find, analyze, and generalize geometric and numerical patterns
- work with order-of-operations rules for arithmetic
- use a concrete model to understand and do arithmetic with positive and negative integers
- work with geometric concepts, including angle and polygon
- write a calculator program to simulate an In-Out machine
- develop proofs concerning consecutive sums, angle sum for polygons, and other contexts

Other topics will arise during class discussions of Problems of the Week.

Materials

You or your students will need the following materials throughout the four-year program:

- a class set of graphing calculators
- overhead projector and screen, blank transparencies, and pens for transparencies
- device for overhead projection of the graphing calculator
- a deck of cards for random grouping of students
- wall space ready to receive student work
- blank attendance chart (classroom layout of desks that can be filled in each time groups change)
- boxes or crates with folders for student portfolios
- tape, glue, construction paper, paper clips, pencils, etc.
- pads of $2' \times 3'$ paper or rolls of butcher paper for posters
- a set of felt markers for each group
- rulers, protractors, and scissors
- bags or other containers to hold materials for each group

In addition to the general list above, there are materials you will need for this particular unit. They are

- four tubs of pattern blocks
- (optional) a set of pattern blocks designed for use on an overhead projector
- lots of beans or similar manipulative to represent objects to be counted
- sets of *Lonesome Llama* cards (one set for each group—see Appendix B)
- manipulatives, such as cubes of two different colors, to represent positive and negative numbers

For a list of materials that students need to provide, see the section "Materials" on Day 1.

Grading

The IMP *Teaching Handbook* contains general ideas about how to grade students in an IMP class. You will probably want to check daily that students have done their homework, and include the regular completion of homework as part of students' grades. Your grading scheme will probably include Problems of the Week, the unit portfolio, and the end-of-unit assessments.

Because you will not be able to read thoroughly every assignment that students turn in, you will need to select certain assignments to read carefully and to base grades on. Here are some suggestions.

- Presentations on *Calculator Exploration* (Day 3)
- *Homework 6: Gettin' On Down to One*
- *Homework 10: Pulling Out Rules*
- Presentations on *Consecutive Sums* (Day 12)
- *Homework 14: You're the Chef*
- *Homework 19: An Angular Summary*
- *Homework 22: Border Varieties*
- Group work on *Stump Your Friend* (Day 23)

If you want to base your grading on more tasks, there are many other homework assignments, class activities, and oral presentations you can use.

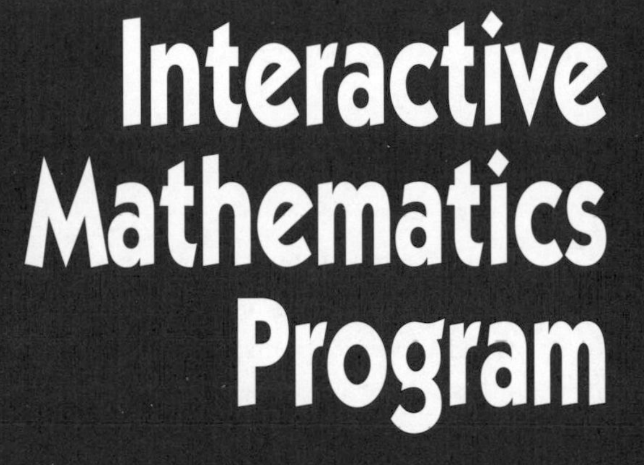

Integrated High School Mathematics

YEAR 1

Getting Started

The first unit of Year 1, *Patterns,* is an introduction to the Interactive Mathematics Program. Instead of a single central problem, this unit has many shorter problems that will help you focus on new ways of learning and communicating about mathematics.

This page in the student book introduces Days 1 through 4.

In the opening days of this unit, you will get started using a powerful tool, the graphing calculator, and be introduced to your first Problem of the Week (POW).

Andy Schultz investigates what his graphing calculator can do.

DAY 1 Getting Acquainted

Students are introduced to each other and to IMP.

Mathematical Topics

- An overview of the Interactive Mathematics Program
- An overview of the *Patterns* unit in particular

Outline of the Day

In Class

1. Form random groups
2. Do student introductions
3. Give students a course overview
   - Introduce the Interactive Mathematics Program as a whole
   - Have students look at *A Brief IMP Sampler*
4. Discuss expectations concerning homework, tests, and grading
5. Go over the list of materials that students must provide, including calculators
6. Introduce the first unit, *Patterns*

At Home

Homework 1: Past Experiences

Note: The introductory material suggested for Day 1 will probably need to be spread out over more than one day. The student introductions themselves are likely to take 40 to 45 minutes in a class of 30 students, and you may want to intersperse these introductions with some of the other introductory material over the course of a few days. However, it is important that students realize early that the Interactive Mathematics Program is different from a traditional mathematics curriculum and that they understand your expectations of them. So this introductory material should be discussed within the first few days of the course.

Discuss With Your Colleagues

The New Curriculum

The main task for Day 1 is to introduce the new curriculum. Students may have varied reactions to the idea of learning mathematics in a different way. Teachers also have varied reactions.

Discuss what the teachers in your department can do to support each other in this adventure. How can you create an atmosphere of trust so that all can share their highs and lows and learn from them? How can you respond to student apprehensions in a positive and constructive way?

1. Forming Groups

Put students into groups as described in the IMP *Teaching Handbook*. We will use the phrases "club card student," "diamond card student," and so on, to refer to specific members of a group, based on the playing-card scheme described in the IMP *Teaching Handbook.*

We recommend that new groups be formed again on Day 13, at the conclusion of the multiday group activity *Consecutive Sums.*

2. Introductions

Tell students that working together will be very important in this class, and their first activity will be a brief introduction to get to know each other.

We suggest that you have students begin by taking about one minute each to introduce themselves to others in their groups. Afterward, each person will be responsible for introducing a person from his or her group to the entire class.

You may want to suggest some possible information for them to share. For instance, students can talk about their families, identify the middle school or junior high school they attended, name their favorite sport, or tell how long they have lived in the area.

After introductions within the groups are completed, proceed around the room and have each student introduced to the class by a member of his or her group.

One convenient scheme is to have heart card students and diamond card students introduce each other, then have club card students and spade card students introduce each other.

You may want to wait until the students get to know each other within groups before telling them which person they will introduce to the rest of the class.

3. Course Overview

"Why do you think there is a new math curriculum?"

"What do you know about IMP? How do you think it is different?"

Discuss the concept of the Interactive Mathematics Program (IMP) with the class. Pose the following question to the students.

Why is there a new math curriculum?

Ask them to share what they know about IMP and about how it differs from a traditional mathematics course. The ideas below should be blended into the students' discussion about IMP.

- *Four years of integrated, problem-based mathematics*

Let students know that IMP is a four-year program of problem-based mathematics and is designed to replace the traditional sequence of courses.

Emphasize that this is an integrated mathematics course, which means that different branches of mathematics are blended together and developed as needed to solve interesting problems, rather than organized into separate courses on algebra, geometry, and trigonometry. Bring out that this integrated approach goes hand in hand with studying mathematics in the context of problem solving.

Let students know also that this curriculum will prepare them for college entrance exams, such as the Scholastic Assessment Tests (SATs), and for college mathematics, and that it contains the important components of the traditional curriculum, such as algebra, geometry, and trigonometry, even though students won't have courses with these specific titles. Tell them that IMP includes some topics, such as probability and statistics, that are not part of the traditional curriculum.

- *A Brief IMP Sampler* *(see next page)*

Have students look over the material in *A Brief IMP Sampler*, either in class or for homework. You may want to briefly discuss the central unit problems mentioned.

> *Note:* For your reference, the IMP *Teaching Handbook* has unit synopses for all four years of the IMP curriculum.

4. Expectations: Homework, Tests, and Grading

Next, discuss your expectations and policies concerning homework, tests, and grading.

For group discussion: "What would you want a math class to be like?"

You may want to give groups time to discuss what they would want a math class to be like, and then ask groups to share their ideas with the whole class. Groups may suggest math classes with no homework and no tests. You can use such statements to clarify the focus of IMP, as suggested below.

- *Homework*

"What don't you like about homework?"

For example, ask students what it is about homework that they do not like. If their response is that homework takes too much time, then you'll have to tell them that they are out of luck in that respect, because they will be expected to regularly do homework that may take considerable time.

Tell students that there are two kinds of homework assignments: daily assignments and Problems of the Week (POWs).

Many teachers say "pow" not "P-O-W" to avoid association of the problem of the week with "prisoner of war."

Talk with the students about the importance of doing the daily homework. Here are some points to make.

- Some of their most important learning will happen when they work on the homework problems. Encourage them to work with other classmates, family members, and friends. To *learn* mathematics, you have to *do* and *talk* mathematics.
- Most of the classroom work will depend on their having worked on the homework. If students fail to do their homework, then they will not be ready to participate properly in class.
- Homework will not simply be a review of what happened in class. Students will often be asked to think about new situations or new types of problems.
- Let students know that they are not expected to be able to solve every homework problem or find every answer. It is especially important for them to realize this when the homework involves new ideas.

Tell students that they will learn more about POWs when the first one comes up in a few days. You may want to tell them now that, despite their name, POWs are not done strictly on a week-by-week basis.

- *Tests*

Since IMP's recommendations on student grading and assessment are different from the usual focus on written tests, you should talk about the role of tests and about the nature of tests in IMP.

"How do you feel about tests?" or "What makes a 'good' test?" or "What should the goals of testing be?"

You might begin this discussion by asking students a general question about their attitude toward tests. Or you can ask what their idea of a "good" test is, or what they think the goals of testing should be.

Discuss the fact that they will be assessed every day in IMP. While this might not sound that great to students at first, explain that it does have many advantages. First, it takes the pressure off. Everyone has good days and bad days, and students will be able to demonstrate their abilities on many days and in a variety of ways, such as giving oral presentations, creating interesting posters, writing clear arguments, and helping fellow group members to understand without telling them answers.

Tell students also that while there is an assessment at the end of each unit, it will not count as heavily as final exams do in traditional math courses. The objective of the program is not to have students briefly master one list of skills and then move on to another list, but to become lifelong learners of mathematics who can discuss and do mathematics. Assessment of student abilities in these areas is much more difficult and must be done in a variety of ways. It cannot be done in one period with a test.

- *Grading and assessment*

This is a good time to talk about your grading policy, explaining how much weight will be given to different categories such as homework, classwork, POWs, and unit assessments, and to reiterate the importance of doing homework regularly.

You can also talk about the distinction between grading and assessment. For example, point out that homework, in addition to being part of students' grades, also serves to give you feedback about how well students are understanding what is going on in class.

5. Materials

Go over with students the list of materials that they need to supply for use throughout the program. This guide assumes that students will provide

- a notebook or binder
- a pencil
- lined paper
- graph paper
- a 12-inch ruler with both inch and centimeter scales
- an assortment of colored pencils or pens
- a protractor
- a calculator

Students need not bring their calculators to class, since graphing calculators will be provided. But they should have calculators available every night for use in the homework.

- *Calculator purchase*

Before students purchase a calculator for home use, you may want to discuss the subject with them so they can make an informed decision.

Although an ordinary four-function calculator will be adequate for the first three units of the year (*Patterns, The Game of Pig,* and *The Overland Trail*), students will eventually need to buy at least a basic scientific calculator. This is required for *Shadows* (the last unit of Year 1).

Also, for *The Pit and the Pendulum* (the fourth unit of the year), they will find it useful, though not essential, to have a calculator that will do statistical

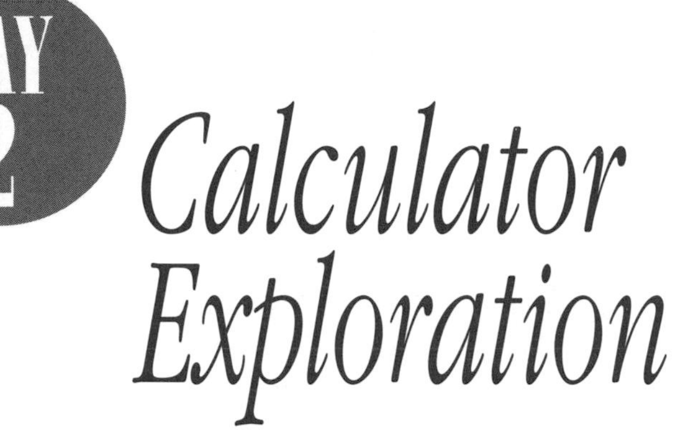

Calculator Exploration

Students explore what their graphing calculators can do and how they work.

Mathematical Topics

- Exploring the graphing calculator

Outline of the Day

In Class

1. Review expectations about homework
2. Discuss *Homework 1: Past Experiences*
3. *Calculator Exploration*
   - Students explore the graphing calculator with a partner (with manuals available)
   - Students take notes as they work so they can share discoveries
   - Presentations on *Calculator Exploration* will be made on Day 3

At Home

Homework 2: Who's Who?

Special Materials Needed

- Calculator user manuals

Discuss With Your Colleagues

Writing and Mathematics

Students will do much more writing in this curriculum than they ever did before in mathematics classes. This poses some challenges to you as a teacher.

- **Do you become your students' English teacher as well as their math teacher, correcting spelling and grammar?**
- **Is it important that this be good writing or does it just need to be mathematically clear?**
- **How do you manage the sheer quantity of student output?**

You may want to establish communication with other departments in your school to talk about these issues.

1. Homework Expectations Reviewed

Before discussing last night's assignment, you can take this opportunity to review the class's expectations regarding homework. As students enter, you can check to see if they have done the assignment. If they all have, you can congratulate them. If not, review what it is you expect of them and what they can do if they don't understand an assignment.

2. Discussion of *Homework 1: Past Experiences*

For group discussion: "Compare your favorite and least favorite classes. Also compare your experiences working in groups and on your own."

Have students pass their assignments around to read within their groups. Tell them that after reading each other's thoughts and experiences, group members should discuss

- similarities and differences in their favorite classes
- similarities and differences in their least favorite classes
- their experiences working in groups and on their own

You may want to put these and similar discussion ideas on an overhead transparency so students can refer to them.

Then let club card students share with the class the common themes their groups encountered in their discussions concerning past experiences and working in groups.

Take this opportunity to reiterate that participation in class—written, oral, and physical; in groups, individually, and with the whole class—is essential for success in this course.

You will probably want to collect and read this assignment, as a way of getting to know your students. As noted earlier, this assignment will be part of the students' portfolios for the unit.

3. *Calculator Exploration*

(see facing page)

Students have a natural curiosity about the graphing calculators. Tell the class that they will have these calculators at their desks every day. Today's class period is an opportunity for them to play with the calculator and become aware of some of its capabilities.

Calculator Exploration

Work with a partner on this activity. Your task together is to learn whatever you can about how your graphing calculator works. Write down what you discover.

Your discoveries might be as simple as how to do arithmetic operations or as involved as how the calculator works with statistics. You and your partner will determine what to investigate.

Tomorrow, you and your partner will be asked to share with the class what you learned.

Learn as much as you can so you'll have something new to add even if your favorite discovery is presented by another pair.

Although user manuals may be available, don't think that you must use one. The idea is for you to explore the calculator your own way. ***Remember to write down everything you discover!***

Students should work in pairs since it would be hard for more than two students to work together on this activity.

You may need to preface this activity by having students turn the calculators on and showing them how to adjust the screen brightness and how to reset the calculators.

The activity is quite open-ended. Let students work on it on their own for a while to give them an opportunity to experience this freedom. But if students are having trouble getting started, you may want to give them a list of areas to investigate. Here are some specific topics you can suggest.

- Entering a calculation
- Deleting a mistake
- Inserting something you forgot into a calculation
- Using the answer to the last problem to continue a calculation
- Working with exponents
- Using parentheses
- Using special keys, such as "2nd" or "alpha," that change the effect of pressing a given key
- Using the mode key

You may want to display these topics on an overhead transparency.

You might even ask students to use the calculator to solve simple problems like

$$3 + 7 = ?$$

or to discover how a certain button works. You should feel free to give them a little structure until they begin feeling confident.

Students should carefully write down which keys they are pushing and the results they obtain so that, by the end of the period, they will have a wealth of information available for their presentations tomorrow. You may want to assure students that their presentations can be simple, for example, "If you press this key, such-and-such happens." They don't necessarily have to learn how to accomplish something useful to make the information worth reporting.

As you circulate around the class, you may want to suggest to specific pairs of students that they prepare a presentation on a particular topic.

Make user manuals available to the students. They may want to use them to learn how to do a specific task or to find out what kinds of things the calculator can do.

Leave about ten minutes at the end of class to introduce the homework assignment.

Note: Some of the topics for investigation in the list above may be unfamiliar to students, but encourage them to just jump right in and try to learn about the topic anyway. Since there is no right or wrong way to approach this activity, they have nothing to lose by experimenting. It is *very* important for students to realize they can learn about calculators on their own, by trial and error, in order for them to feel confident with calculators in the future. Students need to feel that the calculators are their tool and that they have control over them.

[The calculator] *is a tool which the students are at first daunted by—"There are* so *many buttons!" "What is matrix, anyway?" "How do you turn this thing off?"—are typical of their first comments and questions. As we have progressed through the first semester their inquisitiveness has fueled their desire to master the machine. They view it now as within their reach to learn its secrets, which aren't really magic anymore. They seem comforted that they have such a powerful ally in their hands.*

IMP Teacher Charlie Lunetta

Homework 2: Who's Who?

(see next page)

Tonight's homework is an introduction to two categories in the Problem of the Week write-up: *process* and *solution*.

Discuss with the class what is expected in each section of the assignment. Urge them to start taking notes as soon as they begin thinking about the problem, and to use those notes in the *process* portion of their write-up (Question 1).

Edith Hernandez uses her calculator while working on "POW 1: The Broken Eggs."

homework completion. Share your experiences in having students write about their difficulties with an assignment (see discussion of this under the subheading "Homework" on Day 1).

1. Discussion of *Homework 2: Who's Who?*

Give groups about five minutes to discuss and compare how they solved *Homework 2: Who's Who?*

As they do so, you can circulate and check to see who made a genuine effort on the assignment. Tell students that their discussion should not just be about the answer, but also about how they worked on the problem, that is, the *process* component of the write-up.

As you listen in on their discussions, try to locate students who did a particularly nice job on each part of the assignment, and ask them to present that part to the whole class.

Some students may wish to use the chalkboard or overhead projector. You might allow about 15 minutes for the class discussion of the problem, both *process* and *solution*. As the discussion proceeds, encourage students to ask questions if they don't understand something and to challenge each other if they disagree or think something isn't clear.

There are many approaches that students might have used on this problem. Try to get several different methods presented, not so much to identify the methods themselves, but to emphasize that there is a variety of possibilities.

- *Uniqueness and proof*

Presumably, most students will have found the one solution to the problem. Be sure to raise the issue of whether there are other answers, and ask students to explain how they can be sure that there is only one. As with the discussion of methods of solution, you should encourage different approaches.

"What is the mathematician's word for a completely convincing argument?"

After several students have offered explanations of why the answer is unique, ask the class if they are completely convinced by these arguments that there is only one solution. Whether they are or not, ask if anyone knows what the mathematician's term is for a "completely convincing argument." If they don't know, tell them that it is called a **proof**.

Point out that "convincing" is a subjective term, so people may often disagree about whether a particular argument is really a proof. Tell students that they will be working further with the idea of proof in this unit and throughout their mathematics education, and will gradually develop clearer standards about what is and what is not a proof.

Tell the class that mathematicians work hard to take all possibilities into account and to not make any unstated assumptions, and that they generally agree as to what "completely convincing" means. But even people who make a career of mathematics sometimes disagree about the "completeness" of an argument that claims to be a proof.

- *Assessing student writing and reasoning*

We recommend that you collect *Homework 2: Who's Who?* to get a general assessment of your students' writing skills and of their understanding of what it means to explain their process and solution. You can also use the papers as a baseline for looking at their growth over the course of the year.

2. Returning *Homework 1: Past Experiences* and Discussing Portfolios

Note: This discussion should take place when you are ready to return *Homework 1: Past Experiences* to students, since that assignment will be included in their *Patterns* portfolios. You can use any occasion of collecting or returning student papers as further opportunity to talk about portfolios.

Tell students that all the work they do should be kept in their notebook for the eventual assembly of a portfolio. At the end of each unit, they will select for their portfolio work that illustrates the main concepts of the unit. Show students that there are specific guidelines at the end of the unit for making the portfolio. (These guidelines will vary from unit to unit.)

Explain that the portfolios will be used as reference materials, for grading, and for sharing with parents, peers, and mathematics educators. Tell students that they will be able to use their portfolios for help when they take their unit assessments. A portfolio is a record of the student's work and progress in learning mathematics and expressing mathematical ideas.

You may want to remind students about portfolios several times during this unit and occasionally throughout the year. If you have access to portfolios from previous classes, you may want to share them with the class so that they see what a portfolio looks like.

- *Taking notes*

Point out to students that their student book contains only classwork and homework activities, and not "text" as such. They will therefore have to create their own reference materials by taking notes in class and by saving their work on both class activities and homework assignments.

Homework 3 Describing Patterns

Mathematics often involves looking for patterns in various situations.

This assignment involves collections of shapes or numbers called **sequences.** Each shape or number is called a **term** of the sequence, and the terms are separated by commas.

Examine each sequence of shapes or numbers below and look for a pattern.

Then write down a description of the pattern and a method for finding the next few terms of the sequence. Give at least the next three terms.

Note: There may be more than one pattern that fits a given initial sequence.

1. 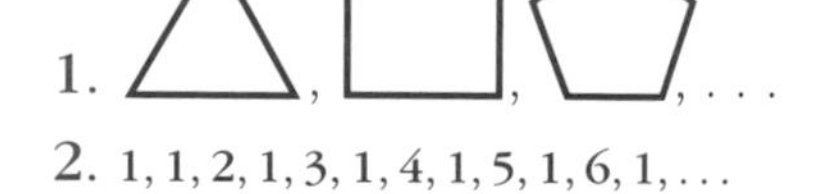
2. 1, 1, 2, 1, 3, 1, 4, 1, 5, 1, 6, 1, . . .
3. 
4. 1, 2, 4, . . .
5. 1, 3, 5, 7, 5, 3, 1, 3, . . .
6. 1, 3, 7, 15, 31, . . .
7. Make up a picture sequence of your own. Describe it by giving the first few terms and telling how you would find more terms.
8. Make up a number sequence of your own. Describe it by giving the first few terms and telling how you would find more terms.

DAY 4

Introducing POW 1

Students are introduced to Problems of the Week and the standard POW write-up.

Mathematical Topics

- Describing geometric and numerical patterns
- Introduction to Problems of the Week (POWs) and the POW write-up

Outline of the Day

In Class

1. Discuss *Homework 3: Describing Patterns*
2. Introduce Problems of the Week
   - Have students read *The Standard POW Write-up*
   - Discuss the write-up categories not used in *Homework 2: Who's Who?*
   - Emphasize that students should begin work on POWs right away and not wait until the day before they are due
   - Students might begin work on the POW

At Home

POW 1: The Broken Eggs (due Day 9)

Homework 4: POW Beginnings

1. Discussion of *Homework 3: Describing Patterns*

While you check off who did the assignment, have students share within their groups the patterns they created in Questions 7 and 8, and have each group pick one of these patterns to present to the class.

Before looking at these student-created patterns, ask for volunteers to discuss Questions 1 through 6. Ask them to describe for the class the patterns they found and the next terms these patterns led to. These descriptions can be very informal, but work with students to make them clear. Students will

The Standard POW Write-up Categories

1. *Problem Statement:* State the problem clearly in your own words. Your problem statement should be clear enough that someone unfamiliar with the problem could understand what it is that you are being asked to do.

2. *Process:* Describe what you did in attempting to solve the problem, using your notes as a reminder. Include things that didn't work out or that seemed like a waste of time. Do this part of the write-up even if you didn't solve the problem.

   If you get assistance of any kind on the problem, you should indicate what the assistance was and how it helped you.

3. *Solution:* State your solution as clearly as you can. Explain how you know that your solution is correct and complete. (If you obtained only a partial solution, give that. If you were able to generalize the problem, include your general results.)

   Your explanation should be written in a way that will be convincing to someone else—even someone who initially disagrees with your answer.

4. *Extensions:* Invent some extensions or variations to the problem. That is, write down some related problems. They can be easier, harder, or about the same level of difficulty as the original problem. (You don't have to solve these additional problems.)

5. *Evaluation:* Discuss your personal reaction to the problem. For example, you might respond to the questions below.

   - Did you consider it educationally worthwhile? What did you learn from it?
   - How would you change the problem to make it better?
   - Did you enjoy working on it?
   - Was it too hard or too easy?

Also point out that the *solution* category in *The Standard POW Write-up* is slightly different from that in *Homework 2: Who's Who?,* in which getting a partial solution or generalizing the problem were not appropriate responses. Unless otherwise indicated, students should follow the description of the *solution* category given in *The Standard POW Write-up*.

You may want to talk about what a "partial solution" might be. You could use the problem from *Homework 2: Who's Who?* to illustrate. For instance, someone might have identified Steve as the ninth grader but might not have known which of the other two people was in which grade.

You may want to post the write-up categories on the classroom wall.

- *General POW work habits and policies*

You can take this opportunity to go over some general principles about working on POWs.

For example, you can tell students that they should not leave this assignment to the night before it is due. In fact, working on the problem a little bit each night is sometimes better than working a lot at one time, because each new look at the problem may provide a new perspective. Suggest to students that they can think about the problem while they wait for the bus or are on their way home; they can talk about it at the dinner table, jot down ideas at the dentist's office, and so on.

Review the fact that they should take notes as they work, since they will need these notes in the *process* part of their write-up.

Encourage students to collaborate with classmates. Tell them that you do not consider it cheating for a student to work with someone else on a homework assignment or POW, as long as they acknowledge that collaboration in their write-ups. On the other hand, students should not be allowed to simply copy each other's work or to let others copy from them.

You can also give students some advice about how to help each other, such as by giving a hint or by asking a leading question. Point out that if they give a friend the answer, they deprive the friend of much of the learning experience.

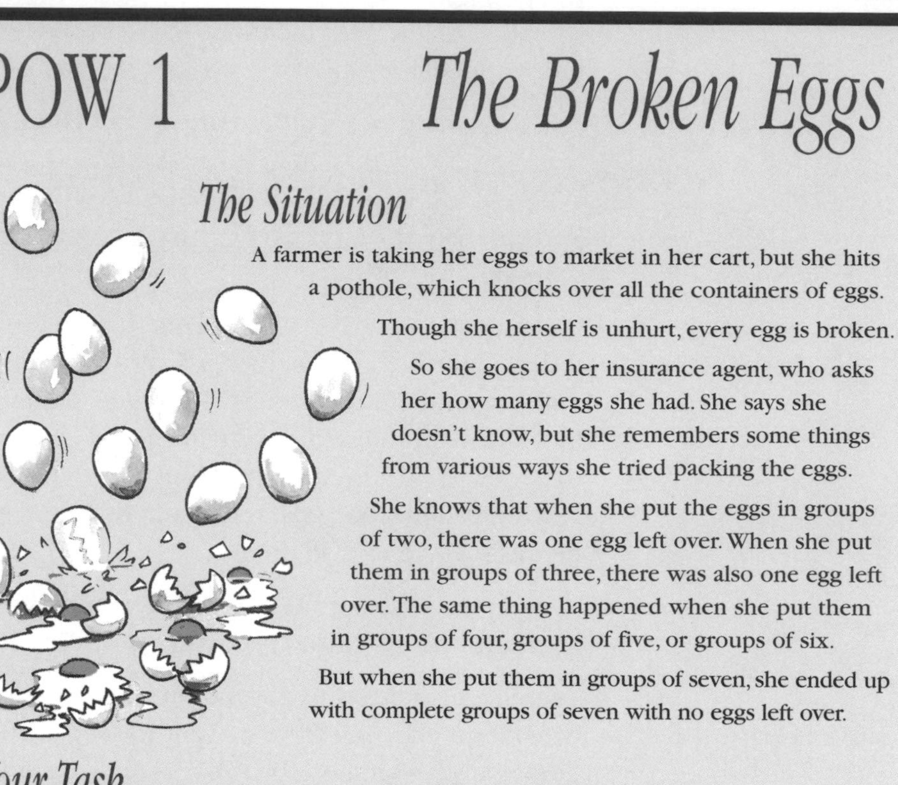

POW 1 The Broken Eggs

The Situation

A farmer is taking her eggs to market in her cart, but she hits a pothole, which knocks over all the containers of eggs. Though she herself is unhurt, every egg is broken.

So she goes to her insurance agent, who asks her how many eggs she had. She says she doesn't know, but she remembers some things from various ways she tried packing the eggs.

She knows that when she put the eggs in groups of two, there was one egg left over. When she put them in groups of three, there was also one egg left over. The same thing happened when she put them in groups of four, groups of five, or groups of six.

But when she put them in groups of seven, she ended up with complete groups of seven with no eggs left over.

Your Task

Your task is to answer the insurance agent's question. In other words,

What can the farmer figure out from this information about how many eggs she had?

Is there more than one possibility?

Write-up

1. *Problem Statement*
2. *Process*
3. *Solution*
4. *Evaluation*

POW 1: The Broken Eggs

Students can spend the remainder of the period in groups, working together on the POW.

As noted earlier, POWs are not done strictly on a week-by-week basis. The curriculum balances these problems with the main work of the unit, and you

Homework 4 POW Beginnings

1. Write the *problem statement* portion of your write-up for *POW 1: The Broken Eggs.*

2. Some students think at first that the answer is 49. Explain why this is not correct.

need not create additional problems in order to have a POW due every week. We suggest that *POW 1: The Broken Eggs* be due on Day 9.

Homework 4: POW Beginnings

This assignment is intended to get students started on the POW.

From Numbers to Functions

In your education in previous years, "mathematics" may have meant mostly arithmetic. By contrast, in the first few days of *Patterns* you haven't been asked to do much of that.

This page in the student book introduces Days 5 through 9.

Joe Gonzales presents his results about an In-Out table.

In *Homework 3: Describing Patterns,* you had to look at some sequences of numbers and make sense of them. As you work on *POW 1: The Broken Eggs,* you will have to think about how numbers behave, rather than just do computations. These problems reflect the perspective that mathematics is not just number-crunching, even when it is about numbers.

Now the unit introduces a powerful tool—the **In-Out table**—for organizing and analyzing numerical information. The In-Out table is a useful way to work with the concept of **function,** which is one of the most important ideas in all of mathematics.

DAY 5

Ins and Outs of Mathematics

In-Out machines are used as an informal introduction to the concept of function.

Mathematical Topics

- Introduction of In-Out machines and In-Out tables
- Finding patterns in tables of data

Outline of the Day

In Class

1. Discuss *Homework 4: POW Beginnings*
2. Introduce In-Out machines and In-Out tables
   - Introduce the terms **input**, **output**, and **In-Out table**
   - Encourage students to guess and experiment
   - Work gradually toward getting clear verbal statements of rules

At Home

Homework 5: Inside Out

1. Discussion of *Homework 4: POW Beginnings*

Let students share their problem statements and discuss whether the statements are clear, whether they repeat the problem too much, and so on.

"Why is 49 not a correct answer for this problem?"

Also have at least one student explain why 49 is not a correct answer. Student response should clarify how well the class understands the problem.

You may want to collect the assignment to get more early information on students' writing.

2. Introduction of In-Out Machines

In-Out machines (also called *function machines*) and In-Out tables will be used throughout the IMP curriculum. Although many students may have been exposed to these concepts previously, others may not have been, so you should start from scratch.

Note: The word *function* is introduced on Day 6, and is used informally later in the unit. There is a brief discussion on Day 6 of what distinguishes functions from general tables of information, and this distinction will be developed further in later units.

You can introduce the concept of an **In-Out machine** with a diagram like this.

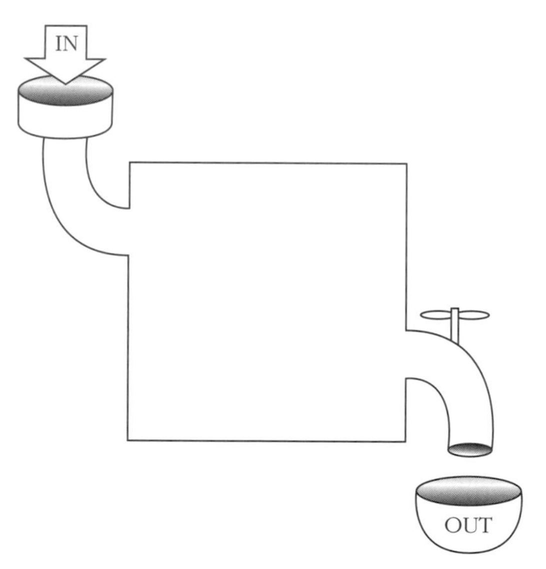

Explain that something, often a number, is put into the machine, the machine does something to that object, and then something comes out. The thing put in is called the **input** (the "*In*," for short), and the thing that comes out is called the **output** (the "*Out*").

With your first example or two, show the inputs as if they were actually being put into the machine and the outputs as if they were coming out of the machine.

"What happens if I put in the number 4?"

A nice way to start is to have students try to figure out what the machine is doing without your giving them any initial information. For example, you can ask, "What happens if I put in the number 4?"

Have various students make guesses, even though they will probably recognize that they can't possibly know for sure. The goal is to make everyone feel free to participate. Give students clues, such as "too high" or "too low," until someone gets the answer that you have in mind. You may want to have several options in mind at first so that it takes more than one guess.

"What number would you like to use as an input?"

Then ask for another number to use as the input and have them guess the corresponding output. Continue in this way, as students gradually get additional information about your "mystery machine."

When most students seem to have figured out the rule, show how to organize the information into an **In-Out table**. For example, you might have a table like this for the "add 4 machine."

In	Out
4	8
3	7
0	4
9	?

"What is this machine doing?"

Ask students to tell you in words what the rule is for this machine. Work toward getting students to express rules in whole sentences such as "The *Out* is 4 more than the *In*" or "You get the *Out* by adding 4 to the *In*," rather than just say "Add 4."

- *Playing with more examples*

Follow up on this introduction to In-Out machines with a variety of examples. (See the subsection "Some sample In-Out rules" for ideas.) It is important that students' initial exposure be a positive one, and that they see In-Out machines and tables as fun and nonthreatening. Be playful in your choice of examples—do not limit your machines exclusively to number relationships. The students need to feel that they can take a chance.

There are various techniques you can use to get everyone involved in this process, such as the following:

- Ask questions like, "What can you do to 4 to get 8? Will that allow us to get 7 from 3?" You want to encourage students to find more than one way to get a particular row of a table, and then to test it on other rows.
- Have those students who have figured out a given rule come up with a good hint for the others, or tell others if a guess is right or wrong.

Once the basic idea is clear, you may want to let students work in groups, making up examples for each other.

- *Some sample In-Out rules*

Here are some nonnumerical examples you might use in which the input is a word.

- The *Out* is the third letter of the *In*.
- The *Out* is the last letter of the *In*.
- The *Out* is the number of consonants in the *In*.

Bring out that in examples like these, we can't use numbers as inputs. In other words, lay the groundwork for the notion (to be discussed tomorrow) that every function has a domain.

Some simple numerical examples include

- The *Out* is five times the *In*.
- The *Out* is seven less than the *In*.
- The *Out* is the square of the *In*.
- The *Out* is ten minus the *In*.
- The *Out* is one more than twice the *In*.
- The *Out* is the digit in the ones column of the *In* (for whole number inputs only).

Some examples that use pictures as the input include

- The *Out* is the number of sides of the polygon that goes *In*.
- The *Out* is the number of eyes of the monster face that goes *In*.
- The *Out* is twice the number of bends in a crooked line that goes *In*.

• *Optional: Further issues regarding In-Out tables*

There are several fine points regarding In-Out tables that you may either wish to bring up now or postpone for a more opportune time.

The goal of this introductory work is to get students to see In-Out tables as an inviting way to approach solving a problem. The decision whether to address the specific issues listed below at this time should be based primarily on how comfortable students are with the introduction of In-Out tables. Remember that students will work with In-Out tables throughout their four years of the IMP curriculum, so let the growth come naturally.

If students express an* Out *in terms of the previous* Out*, you can ask, "What is a rule for expressing the* Out *directly in terms of the* In*?"

"What's the* Out *if the input is 1000?"

• *Expressing the* Out *directly in terms of the* In

Many times students will write rules that express a given *Out* in terms of the previous *Out*. This especially makes sense when the inputs are listed in some organized sequence. Give students due credit for finding such a rule for the table, but urge them to look for rules that express the *Out* directly in terms of the *In*.

One way to motivate students to move in that direction is to ask them how they would come up with the *Out* for a very large *In*. They should see that if they express each *Out* only in terms of the previous *Out*, they would have to work their way up to the large number one step at a time. In some cases, this would be very time consuming.

• *Only one* Out *for each* In

You can tell the students that the *Out* must depend only on the *In*. This means that, if one repeats an *In*, the machine must give the same *Out* as before. The particular order in which *Ins* are used must not affect the output.

However, many different inputs can yield the same output. This will be clear in nonnumerical examples such as "number of letters in the word," and may also come out in some numerical examples.

Note: This issue is scheduled to be discussed briefly tomorrow, with the introduction of the term *function*.

- *Expressing rules clearly*

It is important that students learn to state rules clearly. Asking students to express their rule as "The *Out* is..." may help them organize their thinking and improve the quality of their communication. But it is extremely important that details, such as the precise way a rule is written, not become the focus of this activity. "Stating a rule clearly" has to do with quality of communication, and is important. Writing a rule in a particular way has to do with formalism, and is not important.

In-Out Tables

The concept and use of In-Out tables serves to really make the task of graphing easy for the students.

IMP Teacher Anthony Pepperdine

Brook Lewis looks for patterns and formulates rules by organizing data into in-out charts.

DAY 6

Sharing In-Out Tables

Students continue their informal work with In-Out tables.

Mathematical Topics

- Finding rules for In-Out tables
- The concept of a function
- The concept of the domain of a function

Outline of the Day

In Class

1. Remind students to continue to work on *POW 1: The Broken Eggs*
2. Discuss *Homework 5: Inside Out*
   - Introduce the terms **domain** and **function**
   - Have students share examples they made up as part of *Homework 5: Inside Out*

At Home

Homework 6: Gettin' On Down to One

Note: Allow about five minutes at the end of the day to introduce tonight's homework.

1. *POW 1: The Broken Eggs*—Reminder for Students

Remind students that they should be working on *POW 1: The Broken Eggs* and should not leave it to the last night. Point out that doing a good job on the write-up is as important as actually solving the problem.

Each group can choose two or three favorites from among the tables they created and copy them onto a sheet of poster paper. They should make their poster big enough so that the entire class can see it when it is posted on the wall.

When groups have made and put up the posters, they should attempt to find rules for the tables posted by other groups. Have each group choose someone to write down the rules they find.

"Are there examples you want to discuss?"

After a while, ask the class as a whole if there are specific examples they want to discuss or with which they had difficulty. You can have the group that created the problem or students from other groups give hints on how to find a rule.

Homework 6: Gettin' On Down to One

(see facing page)

This homework assignment introduces students to an easily approachable and engrossing problem involving a situation that is still unresolved by mathematicians.

Take a few minutes to go over the pair of rules by which the sequence is defined, to help students get started on the assignment.

You may want to go over the specific example discussed in the assignment (in which 7 is the starting number) or do a different example.

Homework 6 Gettin' On Down to One

This problem is about a certain pair of rules for generating a sequence of numbers.

You can start with any positive whole number (1, 2, 3, 4, and so on) as the first term. After that, you find each term by applying one of two rules to the current term.

The decision about which rule to apply depends on whether the current term is an odd number or an even number.

- If the current term is an odd number, the rule is

  Multiply the current term by 3 and then add 1 to get the next term in the sequence.

- If the current term is an even number, the rule is

  Divide the current term by 2 to get the next term in the sequence.

Continued on next page

For example, suppose the starting number is 7. Since this is an odd number, you use the first rule: multiply by 3 and then add 1. That gives 22, so the second term in the sequence is 22. Since 22 is even, you now use the second rule: divide by 2. That gives 11, so the third term in the sequence is 11. And so on.

Following the correct rule each time, starting with 7, you generate the sequence

7, 22, 11, 34, 17, 52, 26, 13, 40, 20, 10, 5, 16, 8, 4, 2, 1, 4, 2, 1, 4, 2, 1, 4, 2, 1, . . .

Notice that any time this procedure gets to 1, the sequence will then go 4, 2, 1 again, over and over. So you should consider the sequence to be finished if it reaches 1.

In the case above, where you started with 7, it took 16 steps to reach 1. (The starting number itself is not counted as a step.)

1. Use the pair of rules above to generate and record sequences for each of these starting numbers.

   a. 6 b. 9 c. 21 d. 33

2. In Questions 1a through 1d, you should have found that each sequence eventually reached 1. Find out, for each case, how many steps it took to reach 1.

3. The only starting number that gets to 1 in only one step is 2, and the only starting number that gets to 1 in only two steps is 4.

   Which starting numbers will get down to 1 after only three steps? Four steps? Five steps? Explore.

4. Describe a way to find starting numbers that will produce very long sequences, such as 100 steps.

5. What other observations can you make about how this procedure works?

DAY 7 Marcella's Bagels

Students work on Marcella's Bagels and see a POW-style write-up for this activity.

Mathematical Topics

- Working with a two-part rule for generating a sequence
- Using a variable to express a generalization (this topic can be delayed to Day 8 or Day 11)
- Using manipulatives and other techniques to solve a word problem
- Describing the process of working on a mathematics problem

Outline of the Day

In Class

1. Discuss *Homework 6: Gettin' On Down to One*
2. *Marcella's Bagels*
   - Students use various approaches to solve a "story problem"
3. Discuss *Marcella's Bagels*
   - Let students share methods of solution
   - Use *POW-Style Write-up of "Marcella's Bagels"* as the basis for a discussion of POW write-up categories

At Home

Homework 7: Extended Bagels

Special Materials Needed

- About 100 beans (or similar item) per group

1. Discussion of *Homework 6: Gettin' On Down to One*

As students get settled, have them compare answers for Questions 1 and 2, which should clarify how the sequence is formed. Then have students share their discoveries and their conjectures on Questions 3 through 5 as a whole class.

On Question 4, students probably will have focused on the powers of 2, which go "straight down" to 1. If so, they may come up with a general principle, such as "the number 2^n reaches 1 in n steps."

Students might find this principle but not state it in terms of variables. You may want to use this problem as an opportunity to informally introduce the use of variables. (If you don't do it here, you can do it either tomorrow or on Day 11.) For example, ask for a number that will "get down to 1" in 100 steps, which students should be able to express as 2^{100}. Then ask what number will "get down to 1" in n steps. Casually point out that this is a way to talk about all possible lengths in one statement, and call the process **generalizing**.

Tell students that no one has ever found a number that *didn't* eventually reach 1, but neither has anyone ever proved that every number *must* eventually reach 1. In other words, the question of whether every starting number eventually reaches 1 is an unsolved problem in mathematics.

2. *Marcella's Bagels*

(see facing page)

You may choose to introduce this activity by reading the story out loud or by telling the story informally to the class, or you may prefer to let students take turns doing the reading.

Then have students work in groups on the problem. Let them know that there are bags of beans that they can use to help them think through the problem.

Note: High school students may be reluctant to use physical manipulatives like beans for help in doing mathematics. Assure them that using such a tool is perfectly acceptable and that if it helps them understand a situation or idea, they should welcome the assistance. (See the photograph on page 67.)

When a group has found a solution, you can have them prepare a presentation to answer one of these two questions.

- How did they find the answer?
- How do they know that their answer works?

Reminder: Students should have calculators at hand at all times. Although this activity doesn't require any high-powered computation, one never knows how and when students will want to make use of this tool.

Marcella's Bagels

Have you ever been really in the mood to eat a bagel? There are some pretty amazing things that can get in the way of this pursuit.

Marcella was walking home from the beach one day. She had just bought a big bag of bagels and was going to share them with her daughter Sonya. (Sonya loves bagels.)

On the side of the road she saw two people collecting food for needy families. Well, Marcella decided that she had quite a few bagels in her bag. Sonya didn't need that many bagels.

"Here," said Marcella, "you can have half of my bagels for the needy." The people were very happy to get all of those bagels.

Marcella thought for a moment and then said, "Aw, take one for each of yourselves." So there went two more.

Continued on next page

3. Discussion of *Marcella's Bagels*

After groups have had time to solve the problem, bring the class together to share the processes by which they arrived at a solution. Have two or three heart card students present their ideas. Some students may wish to use the chalkboard or overhead projector.

As Marcella walked along the beach, some surfers came out of the water. They saw, and even smelled, the fresh bagels she had. "Could you by any chance spare a few bagels?" they pleaded. "We are so-o-o hungry after riding all of those gnarly waves."

As you might imagine, Marcella was not thrilled. But she had a good heart and recognized hunger after physical exertion, so she handed her bag to the surfers. They took half of her bagels and then, just as they were about to hand the bag back, they took two more.

Now Marcella was a very reasonable person who liked to help others. She thought she still had enough bagels left to make Sonya happy. She walked on.

As you may already have guessed, Marcella didn't get far before she had another encounter. Just before she reached home, her friend Susan approached. After exchanging greetings, Susan explained that she was on her way to get some bagels for her family. Susan seemed to be in a bit of a rush.

Generosity overtook Marcella and she found herself saying, "Why don't you save yourself the trip and take some of my bagels? As you can see, I've got several." So Susan took half of what Marcella had in the bag and then two more.

Marcella finished her walk home without further interruption. When she opened her once bulging bag of bagels, she discovered that there were only two left! She had a bagel lunch with her daughter Sonya, and then there were none!

After lunch, Sonya asked her mother how many bagels had been in the bag to begin with. Marcella told her the story of her walk and then said that if Sonya could figure it out herself, Marcella would take her rollerblading in the park the next day.

Sonya took awhile, but she figured it out and got her rollerblading outing.

What was Sonya's answer?

"What method did you use to solve the problem?"

Encourage students to talk about all the different methods that they used to solve the problem, such as

- guess and check
- working backwards using arithmetic
- using manipulatives, such as beans
- using some kind of algebraic representation

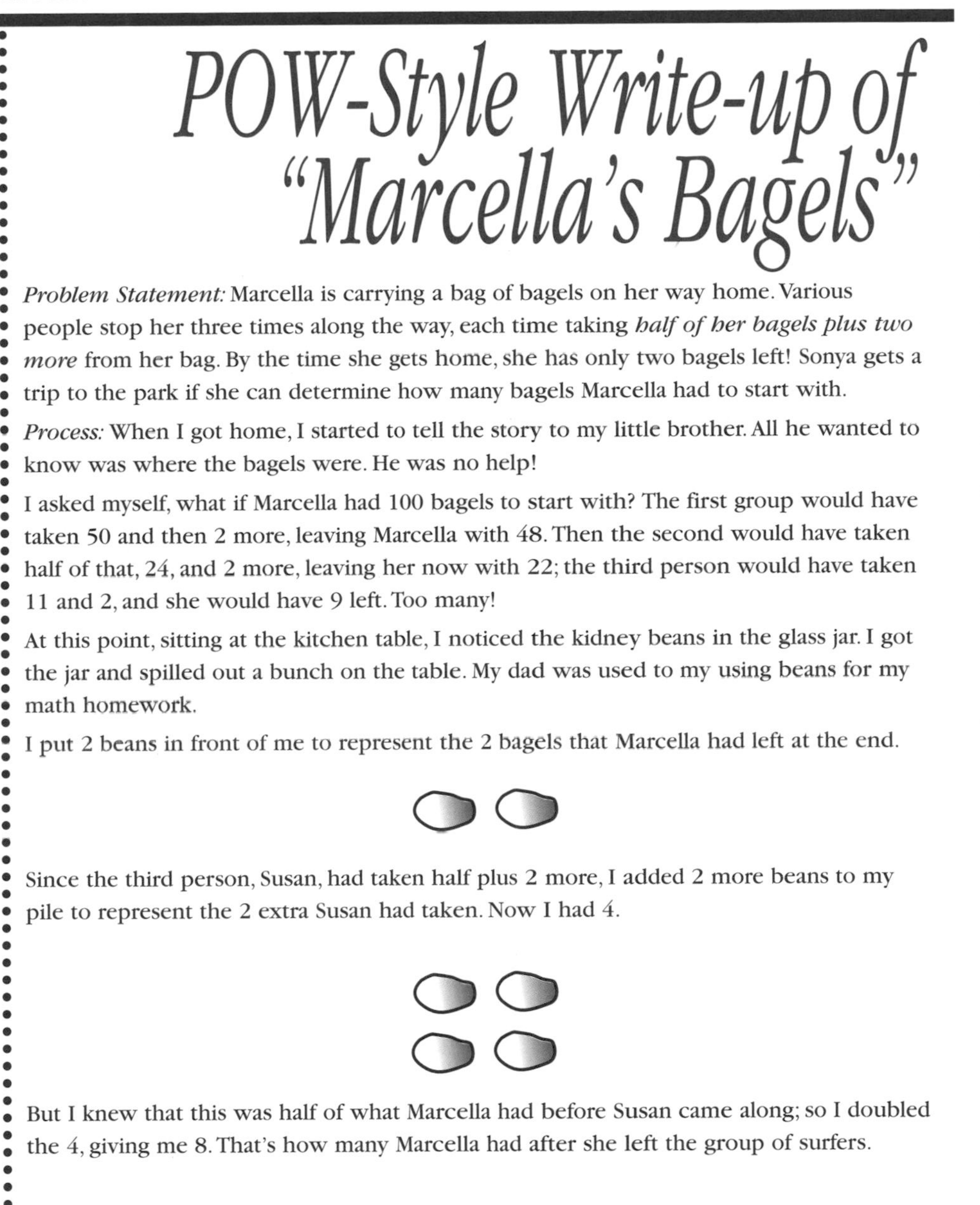

Reference

Patterns

POW-Style Write-up of "Marcella's Bagels"

Problem Statement: Marcella is carrying a bag of bagels on her way home. Various people stop her three times along the way, each time taking *half of her bagels plus two more* from her bag. By the time she gets home, she has only two bagels left! Sonya gets a trip to the park if she can determine how many bagels Marcella had to start with.

Process: When I got home, I started to tell the story to my little brother. All he wanted to know was where the bagels were. He was no help!

I asked myself, what if Marcella had 100 bagels to start with? The first group would have taken 50 and then 2 more, leaving Marcella with 48. Then the second would have taken half of that, 24, and 2 more, leaving her now with 22; the third person would have taken 11 and 2, and she would have 9 left. Too many!

At this point, sitting at the kitchen table, I noticed the kidney beans in the glass jar. I got the jar and spilled out a bunch on the table. My dad was used to my using beans for my math homework.

I put 2 beans in front of me to represent the 2 bagels that Marcella had left at the end.

Since the third person, Susan, had taken half plus 2 more, I added 2 more beans to my pile to represent the 2 extra Susan had taken. Now I had 4.

But I knew that this was half of what Marcella had before Susan came along; so I doubled the 4, giving me 8. That's how many Marcella had after she left the group of surfers.

Continued on next page

POW-Style Write-up of "Marcella's Bagels"

Next, have students find and read *POW-Style Write-up of "Marcella's Bagels,"* which uses the problem *Marcella's Bagels* to illustrate the POW write-up categories.

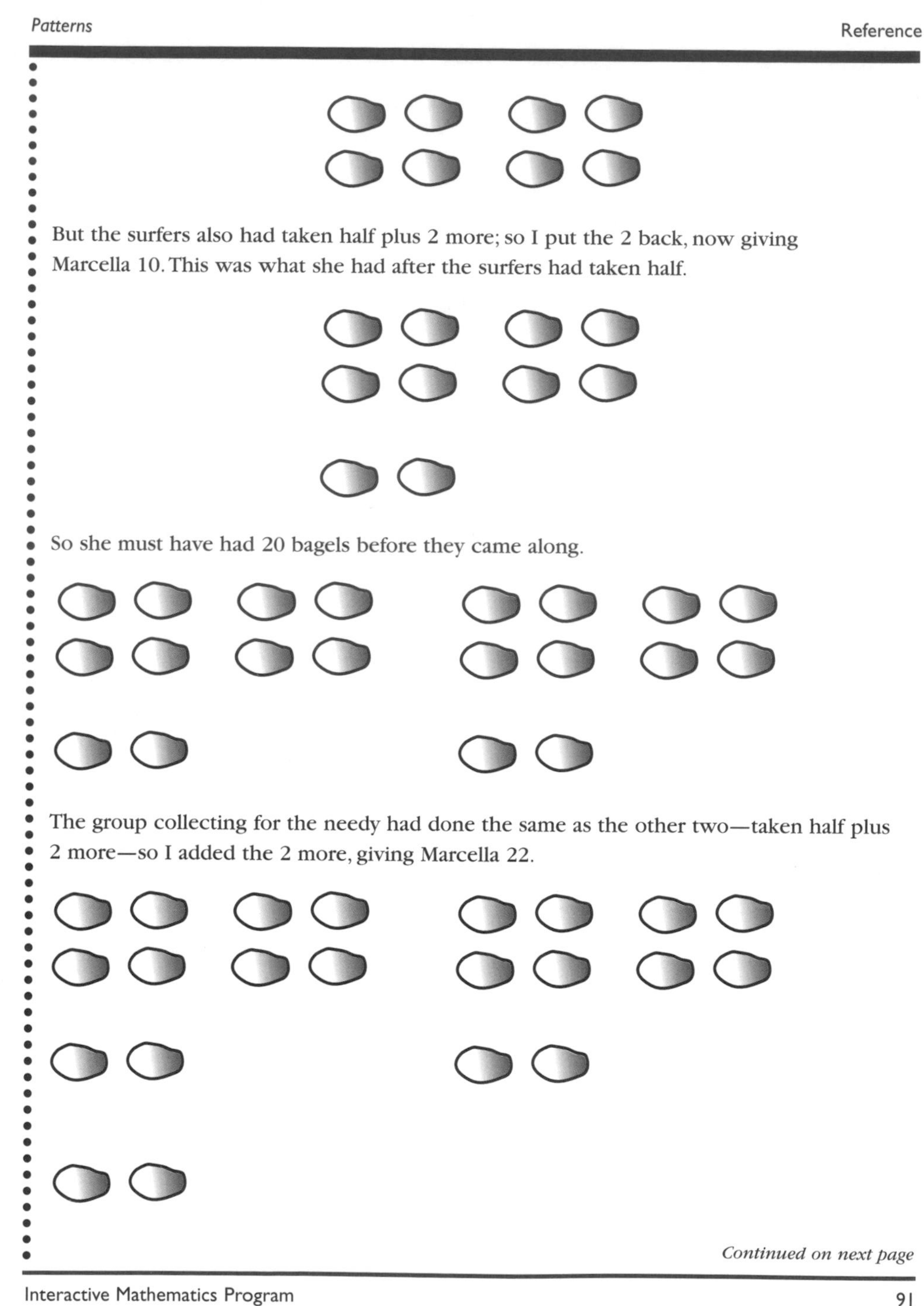

Patterns Reference

But the surfers also had taken half plus 2 more; so I put the 2 back, now giving Marcella 10. This was what she had after the surfers had taken half.

So she must have had 20 bagels before they came along.

The group collecting for the needy had done the same as the other two—taken half plus 2 more—so I added the 2 more, giving Marcella 22.

Continued on next page

Interactive Mathematics Program 91

Note: The reduced *POW-Style Write-up of "Marcella's Bagels"* is included here in this guide. It is placed toward the back of the student materials (as the last of the supplemental problems) so that students will be less likely to refer to it when they work on the problem.

And finally, I doubled that.

This gave her 44 beans.

Solution: So I figure since each bean represents a bagel, Marcella must have started out with 44 bagels.

At this point my younger brother asked me how come I was playing with food again. So, for the second time, I told him the story about Marcella and the bagels and acted it out with him with the beans as I talked.

$$44 \rightarrow 22 \rightarrow 20 \rightarrow 10 \rightarrow 8 \rightarrow 4 \rightarrow 2$$

It really helped to use the beans to be Marcella's bagels. I could also tell that I got the answer because I acted it out, and I came out with 2, which is what she had left. I don't know if another answer would work, but I don't think so since I worked backwards and didn't have any choices along the way. It wasn't like Marcella had fewer than 5 bagels, or more than 1 bagel. She had *exactly* 2 bagels left.

Drawing the pictures I did, I could now explain my process to someone else, using dots. Each dot was a bean, which was really a bagel.

Extensions: What if Marcella had 5 bagels left? What would that mean about how many she had at the start? Or what if she ended with 2 but each group she met took a third and then 3 more? Or what if she met even more people on her way home?

Evaluation: Not too hard, maybe even a little easy once I used the beans. It was fun trying to explain it to my brother. I think I learned something about experimenting and trying things out. I'd like the problem better if Marcella weren't such a softie!

"How does the process here differ from the solution?"

When students have finished reading, have them discuss their reactions to the write-up. Draw their attention to the ways the writer used the categories in the POW write-up. In particular, the discussion should bring out that the write-up describes how the writer *thought about* the problem; it doesn't just present the answer.

Tell the volunteers that the transparencies are to be used to *help with* their presentations, rather than to *be* their presentations. In other words, they should not plan just to read aloud what's on the transparencies, but should plan to explain the problem, using the transparencies to save the trouble of writing as they talk. They can include diagrams, numerical calculations, or whatever they think will be helpful in their explanation.

Also, tell students to plan to talk about *all* parts of the write-up, not just about their solution. Finally, tell them to make any written work on transparencies large enough to be readable.

2. Discussion of *Homework 7: Extended Bagels*

You can have students share within groups the results of their homework. While they are doing so, you may wish to verify that they have all attempted to do the assignment. You can pass out overhead transparencies and pens to two or three groups to present ideas.

> The primary purpose of the homework is to get students used to an exploratory style of thinking. In the discussion of what they did at home, the focus should be on the technique of data gathering. Use your judgment about how many individual cases you need to discuss.

Have the class create an In-Out table with all their data. It might look like the table below.

Number of bagels when Marcella gets home	Number of bagels Marcella started with
0	28
1	36
2	44
3	52
4	60
5	68

Once students have put this information together, ask them what they see by way of a pattern. If the table is organized as above with increasing *Ins*, students will probably see that the *Outs* are increasing by 8. (If they didn't organize the entries for homework, you may want to let them study the table for a few minutes.)

If no one has found (or now finds) a general rule for directly expressing the *Out* in terms of the *In*, you can leave it an open question. You can ask about it tomorrow to see if anyone has found the rule, but don't give hints.

If students find a rule and express it in words (for example, "Multiply the number of bagels by 8 and then add 28"), you can ask for an algebraic expression for the number of bagels to start with in order for Marcella to end up with b bagels. That is, ask what the *Out* would be if the *In* were b. This will give you an opportunity to tell students that we abbreviate $8 \cdot b + 28$ as $8b + 28$. Bring out that omitting the multiplication symbol is simply a convention of notation.

Introduce the word **variable** to describe the role of b. Don't try to give a formal definition of the word, but suggest that here it refers to a letter that is being used to represent a general case. (The word *variable* is used in other contexts to have somewhat different meanings.) Tell the class that $8b + 28$ is called an **algebraic expression**.

Also, tell them that a number used to multiply a variable, such as 8 in the expression $8b + 28$, is called a **coefficient**.

> *Note:* If students didn't find a rule for the table, then you can introduce the notation and terminology just described on Day 11.

3. *Lonesome Llama*

(see next page)

> • *The purpose of the activity*
>
> Group work is an integral part of this mathematics course. Individual students will find that sometimes they take on one role in the group and at other times they take on another. Understanding a bit about group dynamics can make the group a better team and can enable individuals to get more out of the experience.
>
> The main purpose of the *Lonesome Llama* activity is to get students to look at group processes and roles while they are engaged in problem solving. The activity is designed so that everyone must participate in order for the task to be successfully completed.

• *Introducing the activity to students*

It is important that you discuss the purpose of the activity with the class. You can begin with a discussion of *why* you place importance on their ability to work in groups. Talk about the fact that, in the real world, people work together all the time. In fact, many employers consider an individual's capacity and willingness to work with others a major criterion of employability.

"Why is teamwork important in the workplace?"

You can ask students to suggest reasons for this focus on teamwork in the workplace. If necessary, raise the following points yourself.

- Two heads are better than one. Employers believe that they will get better solutions to problems if several people share their ideas.

Lonesome Llama

In the land where llamas run free, llamas live in fancy houses decorated with wonderful shapes.

Most llamas live in houses that look just like the house of at least one other llama. Llamas who live in identical houses tend to play together.

But one llama has a house different from all the rest. So sometimes this llama is left all alone.

If you can help find the lonesome llama, perhaps you can introduce that llama to others.

The Cards

A set of cards will be distributed among your group members, face down. Each card in the set has a picture of a llama's house.

One card in the set is a **singleton;** that is, there is no other card with a house exactly like it. Every card other than this singleton has at least one duplicate.

The Task

Your task *as a group* is to discover the singleton card of the lonesome llama's house.

When your group indicates that they have located the lonesome llama, the task is ended, whether or not you are correct. Therefore, be sure *everyone* is confident of your answer before you declare that you are done.

The Rules

1. You may not show any of your cards to another member.
2. You may not pass cards to another member.
3. You may not look at another member's cards.
4. You may not draw pictures or diagrams of the designs on the houses.
5. You may not put cards in a common pile.

Aside from these rules, you may work in any way you choose.

- Complex problems require communication. Often no single individual or even department will have complete responsibility for a project, so it becomes essential that each person working on it is able to understand what the others are doing.

In keeping with the *Patterns* theme, talk about how traditional mathematics courses value individual work much more than group work, so students get into a pattern of working individually in math class. You can tell students that one goal of this unit is to break those old patterns (if they exist) and to build new ones based on cooperation and respect for the contributions of others.

Tell students that, as they work on *Lonesome Llama,* they should try to pay attention to how they work *together*. Let them know that you will be paying close attention to the interactions within groups.

- *Doing the activity*

Let students read through the entire activity. Before passing out the sets of cards, emphasize that they are not to look at each other's cards at any time until the activity is completed.

Then hand out the sets of cards, face down, to each group, and have students deal out the cards approximately equally among the group members. (Since there are 46 cards per set, students in a given group won't all get the same number of cards.) Each student can then look at his or her own cards.

Although students will have read the rules, experience has indicated that you will need to go over the rules very carefully to ensure that students understand them. So go through the rules with the whole class, one rule at a time, now that they have the cards.

It is especially important to go over rule 5 about not putting cards in a common pile. Explain that if the students put their matches in a common pile, there will be no way for them to backtrack if they see partway through the activity that they have made a mistake.

When a group decides that they have found the unique card (whether or not they are correct), the first stage of the activity is over for them.

Then each student in the group should write about these questions:

- What were your group's strengths and weaknesses in working together?
- How can you get the group to work together better?
- How can you improve your individual contributions to the group?

4. Discussion of *Lonesome Llama*

Once all the groups are done with the activity, you can have students do *focused free-writing* on the topic "What makes a group work well?"

You will need to explain the idea of focused free-writing to students (see the IMP *Teaching Handbook*). There are several key points to make.

- The writing is not collected (but students will have the opportunity to read some of it aloud or just share their ideas).
- The student should write, write, write—a sort of stream of consciousness.
- Students should try to stick with the assigned focus.

Tell students that it is better to write things like "I can't think of what to say" than to stop writing completely.

"Who is willing to share an idea?"

After a few minutes, ask for volunteers to share their ideas. Students may choose to read what they wrote or they may prefer to talk about their thoughts.

As the discussion progresses, you can copy down their suggestions on chart paper and post the collected ideas at the end of the discussion. You may want to emphasize ideas that relate to mutual respect and attention to the task at hand.

An important aspect of this discussion is the recognition that accomplishing a task often involves more than just working directly on the task. It generally requires attention to the *affective* component of the process—that is, how people *feel* as they work—as well as the *cognitive* component, what people *think* as they work.

Note: There is no need to introduce the terms *affective* and *cognitive* into the discussion.

"What happened in your group?"

If students do not talk spontaneously about how they feel, you can prompt such a discussion by asking questions such as the following:

- How did it feel to work in a setting where you needed other students' cooperation?
- How were you treated by the other group members?
- Was everybody equally involved in the activity?
- Did it seem as if some people were "sponging" off others?

Amber Conover and Anandika Muni discuss homework results in their group.

"How might you get someone more involved?"

"What can you do if a group member is 'sponging'?"

Depending on the responses, you can follow up these questions with others. For example, if students say that their group members were not equally involved, you can ask what they might do to get someone more involved. Or you can ask what they would recommend if they find that someone is "sponging."

You may want to broaden the discussion about behavior in groups to extend beyond this specific activity. That is, encourage students to talk about other experiences they have had where they had to work cooperatively with others.

If it does not arise in the students' discussion, introduce the idea of different roles or tasks that are part of successful group work. You should try to draw these roles and tasks out of students, but you may need to get them started. Some suggestions you can make include

- recording results
- being supportive of others' efforts
- offering new ideas
- keeping the group on task
- summarizing
- seeking consensus
- getting clarification
- suggesting compromises
- keeping everyone actively involved
- watching out for and resolving conflict

Tell students that group work, like any other behavior, is something that they can work on during the four-year IMP curriculum. As long as they get involved in their group and respect the other members, then they should see improvement. The age-old saying, "Treat others as you would want others to treat you," might be worth mentioning.

Homework 8 Group Reflection

As you can tell from the activity *Lonesome Llama*, people play many roles when they work in groups. Of course, this is true not only in math classes.

This assignment is an opportunity for you to reflect upon the way you participate in groups. Be as thoughtful as possible when you answer these questions because they are designed to help you.

This homework will not be shared with other students unless you wish it to be.

1. a. Try to remember a time when you or someone in a group you were in was left out of a discussion. Describe the situation. Did anyone try to include that person? If not, why not? If yes, then how?

   b. What might you have done to help with the situation?

2. a. What has been your experience when someone has made a mistake in your group?

   b. How do you think groups should handle mistakes by group members?

3. a. Try to remember a time when you thought of saying something, or you did not understand something, but were afraid to speak out. Describe the situation, what you wanted to say, and why you did not say it.

   b. How do you wish you had handled the situation?

4. Do you participate more or less than other group members? Why do you think you do so?

5. Discuss how the amount of homework preparation you do for class affects your participation in group discussions.

Homework 8: Group Reflection

This homework assignment asks the students to reflect upon working in groups.

You may want to remind students to finish their POWs and bring them to class tomorrow.

DAY 9

POW 1 Presentations and Order of Operations

Students make their first POW presentations and also learn about order of operations.

Mathematical Topics

- Looking at different ways to solve a word problem
- Rules for the order of operations

Outline of the Day

In Class

1. Discuss *Homework 8: Group Reflection*
2. Presentations of *POW 1: The Broken Eggs*
   - Encourage students to ask questions and challenge presenters
   - Be sure students are aware that there is more than one solution
3. Introduce order-of-operations rules
   - Begin with examples so students see the need for rules
   - Post the rules and emphasize that they are merely conventions

At Home

Homework 9: Uncertain Answers

POW 2: 1-2-3-4 Puzzle (due Day 15)

1. Discussion of *Homework 8: Group Reflection*

Let students share what they want about this assignment. You may want to talk about your own experiences working in groups as a way of breaking the ice on what may be a delicate subject.

You may want to collect and read these assignments, not for grading, but in order to gain some insight into the dynamics of your classroom and the specific attitudes of your students.

2. Presentations of *POW 1: The Broken Eggs*

"What is expected from you as a listener?"

You may choose to collect the POWs before beginning the presentations and to ask students to review what is expected of listeners during presentations (see Day 3). It is important to establish good habits early in this new curriculum.

As a teacher, remember that making presentations is very difficult for some students, and these first POW presenters might have a tough time. They deserve special consideration because of their willingness to volunteer.

"Did you have another way to work on this problem?"

Encourage students to ask questions during the presentations. After the presentations are over, ask if other students have anything to add. Be sure that students realize that this invitation also includes presenting a different method for finding or for explaining an answer—they do not have to have a new or a different answer.

- *Other solutions*

"Are there other answers to this problem?"

If the presentations did not deal with the issue of the POW having more than one answer, bring that up now. Many students may have stopped when they found that 301 fits the given conditions, and may not have looked beyond that.

You can simply ask if there are any other answers to the problem. Make students aware that this problem, like many others, has more than one answer, and that, in general, their goal should be to find as many answers as possible.

Important: It is not the goal here for students to find the general expression for all possible solutions, but simply to have them recognize the issue of multiple solutions.

There is a supplemental problem, *More Broken Eggs*, for those who want to pursue this issue further.

3. Order of Operations

The order-of-operations rules are a necessary part of understanding mathematical notation. Though some students may have been exposed to them before, we treat the topic here as if most of them have not.

"Work these problems in your head."

To introduce the topic, you can put arithmetic problems like these on the board, asking students to work on them individually. Have students do them *without using calculators*.

- $4 + 5 \cdot 3 + 1$
- $10 + 2 - 4 + 3$
- $2 + 3(5 + 4)$
- $3 + 4^2$
- $2 + 4 \cdot 3^2$
- $12 \div 4 - 3$

Probably some students will remember the order-of-operations rules and use them to get the correct answers, while others may never have learned the rules or may have forgotten them. In any case, you should expect to get conflicting answers.

Look at one or two examples and ask what answers students got. Go through the details of computation for each answer to see how the expressions can be interpreted in more than one way.

Point out to the class that it would create great difficulties if more than one answer were correct. Mathematicians, scientists, and just about everyone who deals with numbers must communicate with one another in writing. Since people cannot always be present to explain which answer they desire when they write a problem, there is a need for a set of rules that will govern how to interpret any apparent ambiguity in a problem. In particular, calculators must follow detailed rules about how to interpret arithmetic expressions.

• *The rules*

Tell students that, by convention, arithmetic problems are worked out according to these rules:

- Simplify expressions within **parentheses** before combining them with expressions outside the parentheses. (This applies as well to other grouping symbols such as brackets.)
- Within parentheses (or where no parentheses exist), do operations in this order:
  - Apply **exponents** to their bases.
  - **Multiply** and **divide** in order from left to right. (Neither operation has precedence over the other.)
  - **Add** and **subtract** in order from left to right. (Neither operation has precedence over the other).

Students may argue that it would be easier just to use a left-to-right convention. It's probably not worth trying to justify the established convention. If students challenge the rules, you can simply say that they have to learn them, because that's how the world operates.

Be sure that students realize there is nothing wrong with inserting parentheses that aren't strictly required. People often do this in order to avoid any chance of confusion. For example, one might certainly write the expression $5 \cdot 3 + 5 \cdot 7$ as $(5 \cdot 3) + (5 \cdot 7)$. Not only is the latter expression harder to misinterpret, but it's also easier to see the intent at a glance.

Post the rules so that you and students can refer to them when needed. You may want to use a shortened version, such as the one that appears in *Homework 9: Uncertain Answers*.

Some students may have learned the acronym PEMDAS as a way to remember the order of operations. Unfortunately, this memory device reinforces the common misconception by students that multiplication is performed before division and addition before subtraction. Be sure to reiterate that within each of these pairs of operations, the operations are performed as they appear from left to right.

• *Some practice*

"Apply the rules to this expression."

Have students work together in groups to apply the rules to a complex expression. For example have them simplify

$$31 - [24 \div (2 + 2^2) \cdot 2 - 1] + 10$$

Go over the problem until there is consensus about the answer (34) and how to get it.

You may want to have students look at the original problems again in light of these rules. There should be agreement on the answers now.

Give students an example involving a fraction with expressions in its numerator and denominator, such as

$$\frac{8 + 3 \cdot 2}{8 - 3 \cdot 2}$$

and have them work out its numerical value. Explain that although the fraction bar represents division, the expression is not equivalent to

$$8 + 3 \cdot 2 \div 8 - 3 \cdot 2$$

Rather, the fraction bar also acts as a kind of grouping symbol, so that the numerator is the entire expression $8 + 3 \cdot 2$, and the denominator is the expression $8 - 3 \cdot 2$. Thus, in order to use the division symbol itself, the fraction must be written

$$(8 + 3 \cdot 2) \div (8 - 3 \cdot 2)$$

• *Calculators and order of operations*

"Does your calculator follow the order-of-operations rules?"

You can have students investigate whether their graphing calculators perform operations in accordance with the order-of-operations rules. They should enter an expression such as $3 + 2 \cdot 5$ as a single problem and see what happens. They can then move on to more complex problems, including those involving parentheses and exponents.

You can point out that ordinary (four-function) calculators do not allow them to write out even a simple expression like $3 + 2 \cdot 5$, and that pushing the keys in the sequence 3, +, 2, ×, 5 may or may not give the standard result.

Charissa Garcia uses manipulatives to help solve "Marcella's Bagels" (Day 7).

Homework 9 Uncertain Answers

By convention, mathematical expressions are simplified according to this sequence.

1. Parentheses
2. Exponents
3. Multiplication and division (left to right)
4. Addition and subtraction (left to right)

1. **Fix these equations!**

   None of the statements below is correct as written. Rewrite them, inserting parentheses so that the resulting statements are correct equations.

   a. $12 - 8 \cdot 1 + 7 = 32$

   b. $8 - 15 + 6 \div 3 = 1$

   c. $7 + 3^2 = 100$

   d. $24 + 16 \div 8 - 4 = 10$

   e. $20 \div 7 - 2 + 5^2 \cdot 3 = 79$

2. **What could it be?**

   Place parentheses in different places in the expressions below to see how many different values you can make for each expression. Find at least three different values for each problem.

   a. $7 - 5 \cdot 8 + 6 \div 2$

   b. $4 + 9 - 6 \div 2 \cdot 5 + 1$

Homework 9: Uncertain Answers

This assignment provides students with an opportunity to get some practice with the order-of-operations rules.

POW 2 1-2-3-4 Puzzle

You've seen that you can change the meaning of an arithmetic expression by inserting or removing parentheses. Of course, another way to change the meaning of an expression is to rearrange its terms.

This problem is about using the digits 1, 2, 3, and 4, in any order you choose, to create arithmetic expressions with different numerical values according to the rules for order of operations.

Continued on next page

POW 2: 1-2-3-4 Puzzle

The unit's second Problem of the Week builds on today's topic of order of operations. This POW is scheduled for discussion on Day 15.

For this problem, a 1-2-3-4 expression is any expression written using each of these digits *exactly once,* according to the following rules.

- You may use any of the four basic arithmetic operations—addition, subtraction, multiplication, and division (according to the order-of-operations rules). For example, $2 + 1 \cdot 3 - 4$ is a 1-2-3-4 expression for the number 1 (since $2 + 1 \cdot 3 - 4 = 1$).
- You may use exponents. For example, $2^3 - 4 - 1$ is a 1-2-3-4 expression for the number 3.
- You may use radicals. For example, $\sqrt{4 \cdot 2 + 1}$ is equal to 3, so $3 + \sqrt{4 \cdot 2 + 1}$ is a 1-2-3-4 expression for the number 6.
- You may use factorials. For example, 4! means $4 \cdot 3 \cdot 2 \cdot 1$, so $3 + 4! + 1 - 2$ is a 1-2-3-4 expression for the number 26.
- You may juxtapose two or more digits (that is, put them next to each other) to form a number such as 12. For example, $43 - 12$ is a 1-2-3-4 expression for the number 31.
- You may use parentheses and brackets to change the meaning of an expression. For example, according to the rules for order of operations, $1 + 4 \cdot 3^2$ is a 1-2-3-4 expression for the number 37. You can add parentheses and brackets to get $[(1 + 4) \cdot 3]^2$, which is a 1-2-3-4 expression for the number 225.

Your task in this problem is to create as many 1-2-3-4 expressions as you can for each of the numbers from 1 to 25. *Remember:* In every case, the expression must use each of the digits 1, 2, 3, and 4 *exactly once.*

Write-up

1. *Problem Statement*
2. *Process:* Describe how you went about solving the problem. Which numbers did you find first? Did you find any patterns that helped you? What did you do when you got stuck?
3. *Solution:* List the numbers from 1 to 25, giving at least one 1-2-3-4 expression for each. If you got more than one expression for a given number, show as many as you found.
4. *Extensions:* Come up with some variations on this problem.
5. *Evaluation*

Investigating Sums

This page in the student book introduces Days 10 through 12.

Some problems have a simple answer. Others have several answers. Some seem never to be finished.

Over the next several days, you will be working on a problem called *Consecutive Sums.* You and your group will probably not be able to learn all there is to know about consecutive sums in just a few days, but you can look at many specific examples, and you will probably see some general principles. As you grow mathematically, you may want to come back to this problem to see what new insights you can find.

Rebekah Turner presents her group's findings from "Consecutive Sums."

This activity will also give you and your group a chance to apply what you learned in *Lonesome Llama* about working together.

DAY 10 Consecutive Sums

Students begin the three-day investigation activity Consecutive Sums.

Mathematical Topics

- Working with order of operations
- Investigation of sums of consecutive integers

Outline of the Day

In Class

1. Discuss *Homework 9: Uncertain Answers*
2. *Consecutive Sums*
   - Go over definitions in the activity
   - Talk about **summary statements** and **conjectures**
   - Students will continue with this activity tomorrow
   - The activity will be discussed on Day 12

At Home

Homework 10: Pulling Out Rules

Discuss With Your Colleagues

Letting Go of Being "the Expert"

In an investigative activity like *Consecutive Sums*, you may be tempted to share your knowledge so that students can arrive at complete generalizations more easily. After all, you went through years of education and training to acquire all the expertise you have now. Shouldn't you share that with your students?

Talk with colleagues about the purpose of an activity like *Consecutive Sums*. How important is it that students know that powers of 2 cannot be written as consecutive sums? Or that every multiple of 3 can be written as a sum of three consecutive natural numbers?

What else are students learning besides these facts about consecutive sums? What are the important lessons of the activity? How can your attitude about student exploration advance these other goals?

1. Discussion of *Homework 9: Uncertain Answers*

This assignment probably will not require a discussion by the entire class. You can give groups a few minutes to share work on the assignment, and students should be able to resolve each other's difficulties within this group discussion.

If you see common errors as you circulate among groups, you may want to draw the class together for clarification, perhaps calling on individual students to explain a given idea. Clear up any conflicts by having students go through the problem one small step at a time.

2. *Consecutive Sums*

(see facing page)

Consecutive Sums is a multiday activity: groups work on it today and tomorrow, each group presents its findings on Day 12, and students work on proofs in *Homework 12: Consecutive Summaries*.

Students' main product for the activity will be a poster or display of some sort to accompany each group's presentation on Day 12. However, you may want to urge students to keep their notes and take notes on presentations since they may want to include material from this activity in their portfolios.

Students may have difficulty with the open-ended nature of the task, so expect to offer a lot of encouragement and advice as they proceed. The subsection below headed "Giving hints on *Consecutive Sums*" has suggestions for you on guiding the class.

"Can you give me an example of a consecutive sum?"

Begin by going over the definitions in the activity. Get students to give examples of consecutive numbers and of consecutive sums, as well as examples of sequences that are not consecutive. Be sure students see that they are to use only *positive* whole numbers in the activity (even though the definition of consecutive numbers includes zero).

"What is your task in this activity?"

Emphasize that the students' main task is to look for patterns or general principles about consecutive sums.

Point out to students that they may see patterns they are not sure about. For example, they may think that odd numbers can be written as consecutive sums in more ways than even numbers, but they may not be sure.

Tell them that such an observation is called a **conjecture** and that this is just a mathematician's fancy word for "guess," except that a conjecture is usually based on some evidence. (The word *conjecture* is an important one, and you should use it whenever the opportunity arises.)

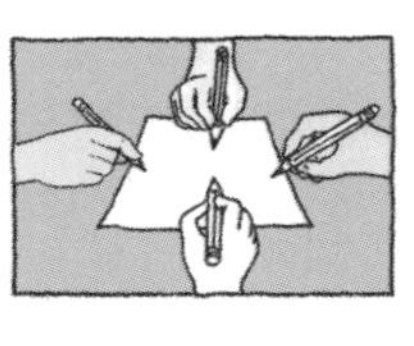

Consecutive Sums

A sequence of two or more whole numbers is **consecutive** if each number is one more than the previous number.

For example, the numbers 2, 3, and 4 are consecutive; the numbers 8, 9, 10, and 11 are consecutive; and the numbers 23 and 24 are consecutive.

On the other hand, the numbers 6, 8, 10 are not consecutive, because each number is *two* more than the previous number. A single number by itself is not considered consecutive.

Continued on next page

Tell students that they should keep track of these conjectures. There are several things that may happen with a conjecture.

- One might see that it's incorrect.
- One might be able to prove that it's true.
- It might remain a conjecture.

A **consecutive sum** is a sum of a sequence of consecutive numbers. So each expression below is a consecutive sum.

$2 + 3 + 4$

$8 + 9 + 10 + 11$

$23 + 24$

These examples illustrate how to express 9, 38, and 47 as consecutive sums.

For this activity, you should consider only consecutive sums involving *positive whole numbers* (1, 2, 3, 4, and so on). These are also called the **natural numbers** or **counting numbers.**

Your task

Explore the idea of consecutive sums. Try to find patterns and make generalizations.

Suggestion: Start by looking at specific cases. For instance, you might work with the numbers from 1 to 35, and try to find all the ways to write each of these as a consecutive sum. Are there numbers for which this is easy to do? Are there any that are impossible?

Note: This is a group activity. Find ways for the members of your group to work together.

Your group should produce a display of some sort on a large sheet of paper. It should show your results and include summary statements of the patterns you observed. Your group will also present some of its discoveries to the class.

Include *conjectures* (general patterns that you think *might* be true) as well as patterns that you are *certain* are true. Include any explanations you find for why your patterns are true.

Also, if you made a conjecture and later discovered that it was false, include both the original conjecture and the evidence that later convinced you that the conjecture was false.

Tell students that, whether or not they are sure of a pattern, they should write a clear "summary statement" of what they *think* the pattern is.

Give them an example of a summary statement, such as "Every number can be written as a consecutive sum." Tell them that while this statement may or may not be correct, it is the type of statement that you will be looking for.

Reminder: Although the arithmetic in this activity is fairly easy, students may find it helpful to use calculators to confirm their work. Be sure that calculators are always within arm's reach of the students.

• *Giving hints on* Consecutive Sums

This activity may be a major challenge to your restraint as a teacher. The purpose of the activity is *not* for students to learn some facts about consecutive sums, but for them to learn how to investigate an open-ended problem. Therefore, you should be wary of the temptation to push groups along faster than they seem able to go on their own.

If groups seem to have no idea how to get started, you can ask them to reread the paragraph labeled "Suggestion" in the activity itself.

If they have gathered some information but are not seeing any patterns, you can suggest that they try to organize the information in a way that might make patterns more visible.

Another constructive hint is to ask what questions they would like to have answered about consecutive sums.

As a general guideline, try to restrict your hints to suggestions about *how* they proceed, and avoid hints that are specific to the mathematics of the problem.

• *Note on grading* Consecutive Sums

Since the primary product of this activity is a group report, it is appropriate to assign a grade to each group as a whole and to use that as the grade for each student in the group.

As an alternative, you might give each group a total number of points based on the quality of its work, and let the group members determine how these points should be shared among themselves.

If you decide to do this, you may want to inform students about the grading procedure when they start the activity.

Homework 10 Pulling Out Rules

1. Write a rule for each of the following In-Out tables.

   Express each rule as a complete sentence, describing what to do with the *In* in order to get the *Out*. Be as clear as you can.

a.

In	Out
10	23
5	13
1	5
0	3

b.

In	Out
1	3
3	17
10	66
6	38

c.

In	Out
3	17
8	12
15	5
0	20

2. The next two In-Out tables don't provide very much information. In fact, there are many different rules that would fit the single pair of numbers in each table.

   Find five rules for each of these In-Out tables. As in Question 1, express each rule as a complete sentence.

a.

In	Out
10	30

b.

In	Out
5	25

3. Read the following problem.

   The supervisor of a community garden project organizes volunteers to help dig out weeds. The supervisor has found that the more people they have, the more weeds get pulled. That's not surprising, but the results are even better than one might think. Although one person will pull only about two bags a day, two people will pull about five bags a day, and three people will pull about eight bags a day.

Continued on next page

Homework 10: Pulling Out Rules

This assignment gives students more opportunities to find rules for In-Out tables and a chance to use an In-Out table to solve a problem.

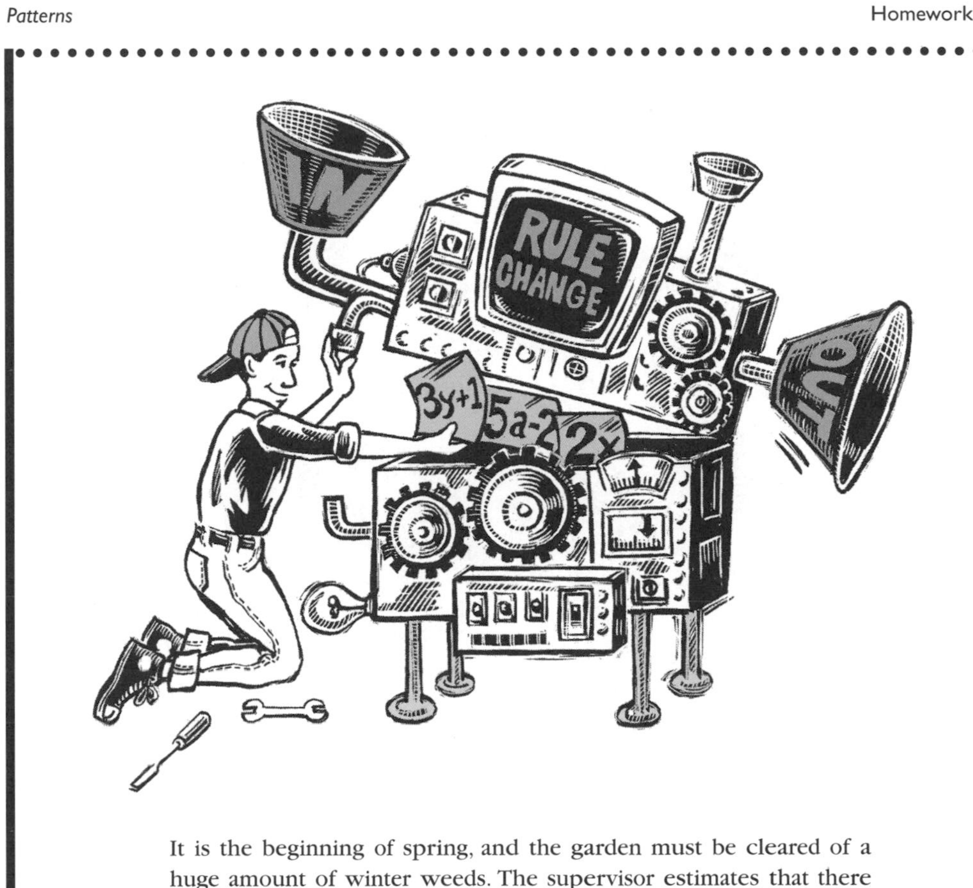

It is the beginning of spring, and the garden must be cleared of a huge amount of winter weeds. The supervisor estimates that there are about 30 bags' worth of weeds to be pulled. How many volunteers would the supervisor need in order to get the job done in a day?

a. Make an In-Out table showing the information provided in the problem, using *number of people* as the *In* and *number of bags of weeds pulled* as the *Out*.

b. Use this In-Out table to solve the problem and explain your reasoning.

DAY 11 Consecutive Sums Continued

Students continue their investigation of consecutive sums, focusing on summary statements.

Mathematical Topics

- Expressing rules for In-Out tables using algebraic expressions
- Finding several rules that fit a single row of an In-Out table
- Continued investigation of consecutive sums
- Introduction to summation notation

Outline of the Day

In Class

1. Discuss *Homework 10: Pulling Out Rules*
   - Have students share ideas on finding rules for tables
   - Students should see that many rules may fit a partial In-Out table
   - Discuss the appropriateness of generalizing from limited data
2. Introduce summation notation
3. Continue *Consecutive Sums*
   - Work with groups to develop summary statements

At Home

Homework 11: Add It Up

Discuss With Your Colleagues

Rules for Finding Rules?

As students gain more experience with In-Out tables, it is tempting to ask them to systematize their approach to finding rules for these tables. But this can undermine the experience of investigation and exploration that is

2. Summation Notation in *Consecutive Sums*

Groups will continue work today on the *Consecutive Sums* activity. But introduce summation notation before students resume their work on *Consecutive Sums,* because it may be helpful in their write-ups.

Start with a multiterm example of a consecutive sum, such as

$$3 + 4 + 5 + 6 + 7 + 8 + 9$$

Tell students that there is a shorthand for writing sums like these, and write out the expression

$$\sum_{i=3}^{9} i$$

Tell students that the symbol $\sum$ is an uppercase letter in the Greek alphabet, called *sigma*, and that the expression is read, "The summation, from i equals 3 to 9, of i."

Let them try to articulate the connection between the shorthand and the full expression. You need to tell them that the letter i is called a **dummy variable** and that any letter would work. For example, the expression

$$\sum_{t=3}^{9} t$$

means exactly the same thing as

$$\sum_{i=3}^{9} i$$

Use a more complex example to illustrate in detail how this notation works. For example, you might use the expression

$$\sum_{w=3}^{7} (w^2 + 2)$$

"How can you 'act out' the process described by this summation expression?"

Ask students what they think this expression means. As needed, act out the process.

- First, w is 3, so the first term is $3^2 + 2$.
- Then w is 4, so the next term is $4^2 + 2$.
- Then w is 5, so the next term is $5^2 + 2$.
- Then w is 6, so the next term is $6^2 + 2$.
- Finally, w is 7, so the last term is $7^2 + 2$.

Since the symbol $\sum$ indicates summation, these terms must then be added together. In other words, students should see that the notation

$$\sum_{w=3}^{7} (w^2 + 2)$$

represents the expression

$$(3^2 + 2) + (4^2 + 2) + (5^2 + 2) + (6^2 + 2) + (7^2 + 2)$$

(This example *does not* show a consecutive sum.)

Point out that although this example does not give a consecutive sum, the values for w itself do go through a sequence of consecutive numbers.

The mechanics of summation notation are summarized in tonight's homework, in which students will work with this notation in geometric as well as in purely numerical contexts. Don't get bogged down on mastery of the notation—it's only intended to be a tool to help students express their ideas.

Note: You may want to introduce the use of ellipsis notation, such as writing $1 + 2 + \cdots + 100$ for the sum of the whole numbers from 1 to 100.

3. Continuation of *Consecutive Sums*

With this notation introduced, have students resume their group work on *Consecutive Sums*. Each group should have a finished product by the end of class today. If a group feels that further work is necessary before presentations tomorrow, group members should decide upon the appropriate homework to do.

• *Developing summary statements*

As students are working, you can circulate and help them focus on the summary statements. The statements below are examples of what they might come up with.

- Every odd number greater than 1 can be written as a consecutive sum of two terms. *Note:* Since only positive whole numbers are permitted in the activity, 1 itself cannot be written as a consecutive sum.
- You can't get the numbers 1, 2, 4, 8, 16, ... as consecutive sums.
- The numbers that can't be written as consecutive sums are all even. (This summary statement isn't correct, since 1 can't be written as a consecutive sum, and it's odd.)
- Every third number—that is, every multiple of 3—can be written as a sum of three consecutive numbers.

Homework 11 Add It Up

Summation notation can be useful when working with sums of numbers, such as consecutive sums.

For instance, we can express the consecutive sum 3 + 4 + 5 + 6 + 7 as

$$\sum_{r=3}^{7} r$$

This expression is read, "The summation, from r equals 3 to 7, of r." The symbol $\sum$ is an uppercase letter in the Greek alphabet, called *sigma.*

Similarly, the expression

$$\sum_{i=2}^{6} i$$

means 2 + 3 + 4 + 5 + 6. (This could also be written as

$$\sum_{n=2}^{6} n$$

It doesn't matter what letter is used.)

Continued on next page

Homework 11: Add It Up

This assignment provides students with a written summary of how summation notation is used and gives them an opportunity to become more comfortable with this notation.

This **sigma notation** can also be used for sums more complex than sums of consecutive numbers. For example,

$$\sum_{t=5}^{8}(4t^2+3)$$

represents the expression

$$(4 \cdot 5^2 + 3) + (4 \cdot 6^2 + 3) + (4 \cdot 7^2 + 3) + (4 \cdot 8^2 + 3)$$

In an expression such as

$$\sum_{t=5}^{8}(4t^2+3)$$

the number 5 is called the **lower limit,** the number 8 is called the **upper limit,** and the expression $4t^2 + 3$ is called the **summand.**

1. Write out each of these summation problems as a string of numbers added together.

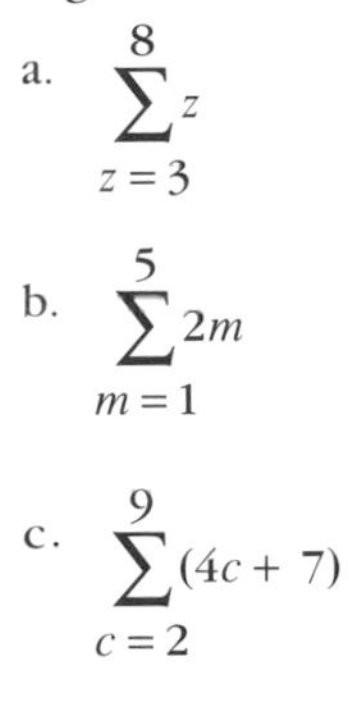

a. $\sum_{z=3}^{8} z$

b. $\sum_{m=1}^{5} 2m$

c. $\sum_{c=2}^{9} (4c + 7)$

2. Use summation notation to describe the number of squares in the picture.

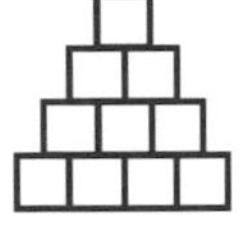

Continued on next page

You may want to remind students to finish any preparation needed for their presentations of the *Consecutive Sums* problem.

3. Use summation notation to express each of these sums.

   a. 10 + 11 + 12 + 13 + 14 + 15

   b. 3 + 6 + 9 + 12 + 15 + 18 + 21

   c. 8 + 11 + 14 + 17 + 20

4. Use summation notation to describe the total number of small squares in the picture.

DAY 12

Consecutive Sums Presentations

Groups make their presentations on Consecutive Sums.

Mathematical Topics

- Working with summation notation
- Summarizing results about consecutive sums

Outline of the Day

In Class

1. Remind students to be working on *POW 2: 1-2-3-4 Puzzle*
2. Discuss *Homework 11: Add It Up*
3. Presentations on *Consecutive Sums*
   - Groups present their summary statements
   - Introduce the term **counterexample**

At Home

Homework 12: That's Odd!

1. *POW 2: 1-2-3-4 Puzzle*—Reminder for Students

"How are you doing on your POW?"

You may want to remind students that they should be working on *POW 2: 1-2-3-4 Puzzle*. This POW is easy to do a little at a time, since it essentially consists of many separate problems.

2. Discussion of *Homework 11: Add It Up*

Give groups time to compare answers and discuss the homework. Next, call on the club card members of different groups to each report on one of the problems.

On Question 2, students will probably see the picture in terms of the sum 1 + 2 + 3 + 4 and use an expression like

$$\sum_{i=1}^{4} i$$

(The number of squares could correctly be written as 3 + 7 or as other combinations, but this isn't likely to come up.)

The expressions in Question 3 could be written in various ways. Question 3c is especially likely to lead to different answers, such as

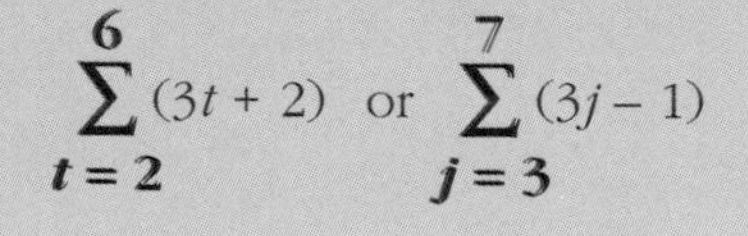

You can leave this question open if students cannot find a way to write the expression using summation notation.

On Question 4, the diagram suggests the idea of a sum of squares and can be written as something like

$$\sum_{n=1}^{5} n^2$$

As noted yesterday, you should not let the class get bogged down trying to master summation notation. Students will learn to work with it more easily as they find situations where it is useful.

3. Presentations on *Consecutive Sums*

Each group should have some sort of poster showing its results and summary statements for the *Consecutive Sums* activity. You can have groups post their work on the wall.

When every group is ready, ask the diamond card member of each group to state one of the patterns that the group found that hasn't yet been mentioned. Keep going around the room (switching suits with each new round) until no group has summary statements that haven't already been mentioned. You may find it best to have all of the statements read before getting into discussion or challenges to any of them.

Then let students comment on the summary statements of other groups. They may have facts that contradict a given statement, or they may simply question whether a given generalization is valid.

Note: If students offer explanations of why any of these statements are true, you can discuss or get reactions to these proposed explanations. But don't push this, because it is the focus of tonight's homework.

Introduce the word **counterexample** in the context of these summary statements, by asking if there are any cases where the generalization doesn't hold.

"What's an example of a false summary statement?"

This term will become clearer if someone proposes a summary statement that is actually false. (If this doesn't happen, you can suggest one yourself.) For example, one proposed summary statement might be "If a number can be written in three or more ways as a consecutive sum, then it must be odd." This statement is incorrect, and the number 30 is a counterexample.

Use this or something similar to illustrate what a counterexample is. In this case, the number 30 fits the condition that "it can be written in three or more ways as a consecutive sum," but it doesn't have the desired property "it must be odd." So the "if…, then…" statement is false, and 30 is a counterexample. (The concept of *counterexample* is referred to in tonight's homework and again in the discussion of the Day 18 activity, *Degree Discovery*. Students will work further this year with "if…, then…" statements in the *Shadows* unit.)

On the basis of this discussion, the class may eliminate some of the summary statements. Others may be confirmed, while still others will remain conjectures. For example, the statement that powers of 2 cannot be written as consecutive sums of positive whole numbers probably requires more algebra skill than students yet have, but the statement is true.

Erin Kadotani explains one of her group's summary statements in "Consecutive Sums."

Homework 12 That's Odd!

A student who worked on the consecutive sum problem made the following conjecture, based on many examples:

> *Any odd number greater than 1 can be written as the sum of two consecutive numbers.*

If you think that this statement is false, your task is to find a counterexample. That is, find an odd number greater than 1 that *cannot* be written as the sum of two consecutive numbers.

If you think that the statement is true, your task is to create a set of general instructions for writing an odd number greater than 1 as the sum of two consecutive numbers. Your instructions should work for *any* odd number greater than 1.

Important: Remember that in *Consecutive Sums,* you are working only with *positive* whole numbers.

Homework 12: That's Odd!

Tonight's homework asks students to develop a general argument to explain a phenomenon concerning consecutive sums that most students will have already observed.

You may want to remind students to use only *positive* whole numbers in this assignment.

Both Positive and Negative

You've probably heard about negative numbers before. You may even have learned some tricks or rules for how to work with them.

The Chef's Hot and Cold Cubes introduces you to an amusing new way to think about positive and negative numbers. Say goodbye to rules and start "cooking" with the integers.

This page in the student book introduces Days 13 and 14.

Tenley McGurk describes her group's explanation for computing with positive and negative numbers.

DAY 13 Hot and Cold Cubes

Students look at proofs concerning consecutive sums and learn a concrete model for thinking about positive and negative numbers.

Mathematical Topics

- Proving general statements
- Developing a model for arithmetic operations with positive and negative integers

Outline of the Day

In Class

1. Form new random groups
2. Discuss *Homework 12: That's Odd!*
   - Look at how a proof uses ideas from individual examples
   - Focus on *generality* as a crucial element of a proof
3. Introduce negative numbers
   - Go over basic terms like **sign**, **opposite**, and **integer** and review use of the number line as a visual model
   - Discuss the meaning of inequality symbols when negative numbers are involved
4. *The Chef's Hot and Cold Cubes*
   - Introduce students to a model for thinking about positive and negative numbers
   - Have students use manipulatives to illustrate cancellation
   - No whole-class discussion is needed for the problems at the end of the activity

At Home

Homework 13: Do It the Chef's Way

Special Materials Needed

- A set of manipulatives, such as cubes of two different colors, to represent positive and negative numbers

Discuss With Your Colleagues

A Model for Negative Numbers

The hot-and-cold-cube model introduced in *The Chef's Hot and Cold Cubes* may be a new way for you to think about integers. As with some other topics, it may be tempting to summarize the activity into a few basic rules of arithmetic for dealing with signs.

Discuss with other teachers your own experience learning mathematical rules, such as those you may have seen in a calculus class. Did you memorize them? Did you ever forget which rule to apply or get two rules confused? Did the rules make sense to you? Do you remember and are you comfortable with those rules now?

1. Form New Groups

Completion of the *Consecutive Sums* activity marks a good time to form new groups. (See the IMP *Teaching Handbook* for details.) You will probably want to wait to do this until after today's homework discussion, which culminates this multiday activity.

2. Discussion of *Homework 12: That's Odd!*

Note: The purpose of the homework is *not* for students to learn a proof that odd numbers greater than 1 can be written as a sum of two consecutive numbers. Rather, it is intended to help students

- begin to learn what a proof is
- learn to distinguish between specific examples and a general argument
- gain experience in communicating complex, abstract ideas
- become familiar with a more precise way of thinking than they have encountered before

"Is the conjecture in the homework true? How confident are you about that?"

You can begin the discussion by asking the class whether they think the conjecture in the homework is true; then ask how confident they are that it is really true for *every* odd number geater than 1. Probably most will be fairly sure of the fact that it is always true, but encourage the skeptics to voice their opinions as well.

Then ask for volunteers to share any general methods they found for describing how to write an arbitrary odd number as a sum of two consecutive numbers. If the class is at a loss how to do this, you might ask a series of questions, such as

- How would you write 397 as the sum of two consecutive numbers?
- How would you write 4913 as the sum of two consecutive numbers?
- How would you write 157,681 as the sum of two consecutive numbers?

Get students to explain how they find the pair of consecutive integers in each case, since mimicking the specific cases is the key to a general argument. You might want to throw in an even number, both to keep them on their toes and to give them an opportunity to see why their methods don't work in that case.

There are several ways to describe the general process, and you should elicit as many as possible from your students. Here are some of the commonly suggested procedures.

- Subtract 1 from the odd number to get an even number. Divide this even number by 2, and then use that quotient and the next number for your consecutive sum.
- Divide the odd number by 2, getting "something and a half." Use the whole numbers just above and below this mixed number for your consecutive sum.
- Add 1 to the odd number to get an even number. Divide this even number by 2, and then use that quotient and the previous number for your consecutive sum.

Note: Careful examination of any of these methods will show that they don't work if the initial odd number is 1, because one of the numbers in the consecutive sum will be 0 rather than a positive whole number as required.

Whichever methods students suggest, try to get them to explain how they know that a given method works. While assuring them that these procedures contain the essence of a proof, help them become aware of the subtle assumptions they may be making.

For example, with the first procedure above, you can ask how they know that subtracting 1 from an odd number gives an even number.

The best possible response to this question would be one that talks about the definition of the term *odd*. That is, students should recognize that, ultimately, you can't say anything for sure about odd numbers unless you know exactly what they are.

Similarly, you can ask students how they know that dividing an even number by 2 gives a whole number result. Again, try to get them to see that the answer to this challenge depends on having a precise definition of the term *even*.

Important: It is not necessary to go into formalities here about the meaning of the terms *odd* and *even*. What is important is a recognition of the value of having a precise definition if one is to give a complete proof.

A supplemental problem, *Three in a Row,* asks students to investigate which numbers can be expressed as a consecutive sum with three terms, to prove their conjecture, and then to generalize the result.

- *What's a "real" proof?*

Use the discussion above to help bring out the difference between a collection of examples of a phenomenon and a legitimate general proof. A proof does not need to utilize algebraic symbols. For example, when appropriate and precise definitions are given for *odd* and *even*, the arguments above constitute completely legitimate proofs that every odd number can be written as a consecutive sum with two terms.

Help students to see that these arguments are better than just giving a few examples such as 23 = 11 + 12, 47 = 23 + 24, and so forth.

Each of the procedures outlined above demonstrate that every odd number is expressible as a consecutive sum of two terms by showing *how to do it,* that is, how to find the two terms. "How to" arguments such as these are considered perfectly legitimate proofs. (They are known as **constructive proofs**.)

Note: Algebraic symbols do sometimes help students to understand, and your students may be able to express the arguments above symbolically. For example, if you use n for the number you get after subtracting 1 and dividing by 2, they can probably write the next number as $n + 1$.

3. Introduction to Negative Numbers

- *Motivating students to use a model*

Some of the examples of In-Out tables that students have seen may have suggested the need for negative numbers. So you should not have difficulty getting students to appreciate the need to do arithmetic involving negative numbers.

What probably will be difficult is getting students to want to do anything other than memorize a collection of rules. Many students were probably exposed to the basics of using negative numbers in previous mathematics classes or elsewhere. They may think that they already know what they need to know and may be reluctant to learn another way of thinking about this topic.

"What do you know about negative numbers?"

"Can you find the answer to –3 • –5? How do you know your answer is right?"

You might begin by asking students what they know about negative numbers. You can also give them a problem such as -3 • -5 and see whether they can find the correct answer and explain their work. Although some students may know or be able to guess the answer, they will probably have trouble explaining why the product of two negative numbers is positive.

The intent of this introductory challenge is to convince students that they still have something to learn about working with negative numbers and that it might be worthwhile to learn an approach that doesn't rely on memorizing rules.

You may even want to give students a similar problem in a couple of days to see whether they have a clearer understanding of arithmetic with negative numbers.

- *Teacher overview*

Rather than simply review the rules, *The Chef's Hot and Cold Cubes* will give students a concrete model for understanding the basic ideas. This model will give them a frame of reference for the rules, and will allow them, if necessary, to reconstruct the rules for themselves in the future.

This topic will be developed over two days, and then followed up in subsequent activities. Today, after a brief introduction, students will read *The Chef's Hot and Cold Cubes* and work in groups on the problems at the end of the story, using manipulatives to represent the cubes.

• *Reviewing the basics*

Before students start the activity, review the notation and terminology of positive and negative numbers. The activity uses "raised sign" notation such as $^{+}5$ for positive numbers and $^{-}7$ for negative numbers. These should be read as *positive five* and *negative seven*, and not as "plus five" or "minus seven." Using clearly defined terminology helps students to distinguish between the concepts of positive and negative numbers and the operations of addition and subtraction.

To emphasize this distinction, negative numbers in today's material (including tonight's homework) are written with the negative sign slightly raised. For example, we write the number called "negative seven" as $^{-}7$ rather than as -7.

Tell students that in most contexts, negative numbers are written using the same symbol as the subtraction sign. Similarly, tell them that in ordinary use, mathematicians don't use the raised plus sign prefix for positive numbers, but that in learning to work with positive and negative numbers, students may find this extra symbol helpful. After tomorrow's discussion of tonight's homework, teacher notes and student materials will use the minus sign for negative numbers and will completely drop use of the raised plus sign prefix for positive numbers.

There are several other items of terminology and notation that you need to review with students.

- The **sign** of a number indicates whether it is positive or negative. Zero is considered neither positive nor negative.
- A pair of numbers such as $^{+}3$ and $^{-}3$ are sometimes called **opposites**. That is, $^{-}3$ is the opposite of $^{+}3$, and $^{+}3$ is the opposite of $^{-}3$.
- The word **integer** means a number that is either zero, a natural number, or the opposite of a natural number. (The term *natural number* was used in *Consecutive Sums*.)

Thus, the set of integers is

$$\{\ldots, {}^{-}3, {}^{-}2, {}^{-}1, 0, {}^{+}1, {}^{+}2, {}^{+}3, \ldots\}$$

- The **number line** is a way to picture both positive and negative numbers. Point out that by convention positive numbers are on the right and negative numbers on the left.

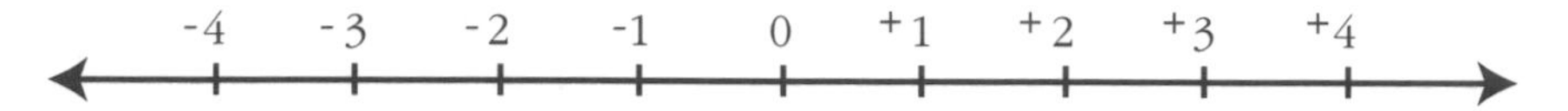

- By the convention just described, numbers are considered to get bigger as they go to the right on the number line.

  Thus, for example, we write

  $${}^{+}5 > {}^{-}8 \text{ and } {}^{-}7 < {}^{-}3$$

  In particular, any positive number is greater than any negative number. (If students are not comfortable with the $>$ and $<$ symbols, this is a good opportunity to review their use.)

You should point out that the basic operations for *natural* numbers are defined, at least intuitively, in terms of putting sets of objects together or taking objects away from a set, but that this type of definition doesn't really make sense with *negative* numbers. Therefore, when negative numbers were invented, people had to *decide* how they wanted the operations to work with these numbers.

To some extent, therefore, the extension of arithmetic from natural numbers to integers is a matter of *convention*. However, there are excellent reasons, both mathematical and practical, for adopting the conventions that we have, and students will explore some of those reasons.

4. *The Chef's Hot and Cold Cubes*

(see facing page)

Have students read the preface and the first five paragraphs of "The Story" from *The Chef's Hot and Cold Cubes* (through the end of the paragraph that starts "If the number of cold cubes...").

Then introduce them to the manipulatives for hot and cold cubes, with one item representing a hot cube and the other representing a cold cube.

Ask them to use these objects to create several different cauldrons, each representing a temperature of 0°. That should introduce them to the idea that a hot cube and a cold cube cancel each other out in some sense.

Then have them read another paragraph (beginning "For each hot cube..."), and have them create cauldrons for other specific temperatures, such as ${}^{+}5°$ or ${}^{-}3°$. The idea is for them to get a sense of the cancellation mechanism and to see that any given temperature can be represented in many ways.

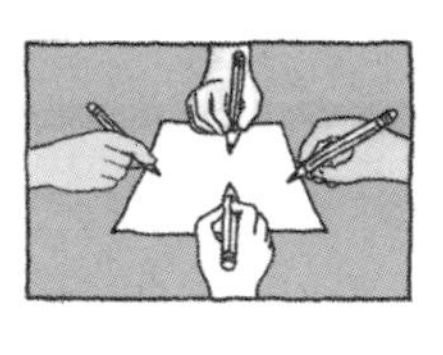

The Chef's Hot and Cold Cubes

You may have learned some rules for doing arithmetic with positive and negative numbers. Many people find these rules hard to remember and don't understand where the rules come from.

The following mythical story provides a context for understanding how positive and negative numbers work. Many people find it easy to remember the story many years after they first heard it, and the memory of the

Continued on next page

After this introduction, let students continue with the activity. You may want to suggest that they read the rest of the story individually and then work in groups on the problems at the end of the activity.

You do not need to discuss this activity as a whole class unless you find that there is some common confusion that is best dealt with that way.

Homework 13 Do It the Chef's Way

Explain each problem in terms of the model of hot and cold cubes.

Your explanation should describe the action and state how the temperature changes overall in each case.

1. $^{-}6 + ^{-}9$
2. $^{-}7 - ^{-}10$
3. $^{+}5 \cdot ^{-}2$
4. $^{-}4 - ^{+}6$
5. $^{+}3 + ^{-}7$
6. $^{-}6 \cdot ^{+}9$
7. $^{-}3 \cdot ^{-}4$
8. $^{+}8 - ^{-}12$
9. $^{-}12 + ^{+}5$

Homework 13: Do It the Chef's Way

The purpose of this homework is to give students more experience working with the hot-and-cold-cube model.

DAY 14 The Chef and Patterns

Students use both the hot-and-cold-cube model and numerical patterns to understand arithmetic with integers.

Mathematical Topics

- Understanding arithmetic operations with integers through the use of a model and through number patterns
- Introduction to absolute value

Outline of the Day

In Class

1. Select presenters for tomorrow's discussion of *POW 2: 1-2-3-4 Puzzle*
2. Discuss *Homework 13: Do It the Chef's Way*
   - Focus on using the model to explain arithmetic
   - Introduce the concept of **absolute value** and its notation
3. Use patterns as an alternate explanation of rules for operations with negative numbers

At Home

Homework 14: You're the Chef

1. POW Presentation Preparation

Presentations of *POW 2: 1-2-3-4 Puzzle* are scheduled for tomorrow. Choose three students to make POW presentations, and give them overhead pens and transparencies to take home to use in their preparations.

Since the 1-2-3-4 expressions are not of that much interest in themselves, urge presenters to plan to talk about how they approached the task, what they did if they got stuck, what patterns or tricks they found, and so forth.

2. Discussion of *Homework 13: Do It the Chef's Way*

Have the heart card member of each group explain one of the answers to the whole class. Insist that explanations utilize the hot-and-cold-cube model, even if students prefer just to quote arithmetic rules to get the answers.

For example, on Question 4, you would like a student to say something like this:

> The $^-4$ [read as *negative four*] means that they put in four cold cubes, which lowered the temperature by 4°. The $-^+6$ [read as *minus positive six*] means that they took out six hot cubes, which lowered the temperature by 6°.
>
> Altogether the temperature went down by 10°. So in terms of the model, we have $^-4 - {}^+6 = {}^-10$.

Some students may comment that taking out hot cubes has the same effect as putting in cold cubes. That's fine, and you should encourage alternate explanations of the individual examples in terms of the model.

Similarly, in a problem like $^+5 \cdot {}^-2$ (Question 3), students may say that the answer is negative "because a positive times a negative makes a negative." Have students explain the situation in terms of the model. For example, they can say something like, "This is as if the chef was putting in bunches of cold cubes, which makes the temperature colder."

Note: Some students may resist use of the model and insist that they can get the answers more easily from rules. You can tell them that part of learning mathematics is understanding and being able to explain it. You can also tell them that being able to explain simple situations like this is good practice for explaining more complex problems.

Point out to students that they do not have to use the model for every computation that they do, but they should be prepared to explain their work in terms of the model when explicitly asked to do so.

- ### *Absolute Value*

Use the discussion of the homework as an opportunity to introduce the term **absolute value**. You can explain it in terms of the hot-and-cold-cube model, telling students that the absolute value of an integer is the number of cubes it represents.

Help students to see that any integer except zero is a combination of a sign and an absolute value. Also introduce the notation for absolute value through examples, such as $|5| = 5$, $|^-7| = 7$, $|0| = 0$.

Note: The concept of absolute value will be used in *The Pit and the Pendulum* (the fourth unit of Year 1) in connection with measurements of data spread.

- *Signs and operations*

"What's the difference between the operation of subtraction and the negative sign?"

Ask students to discuss the difference between an operation and a sign, and have them identify each in the homework problems.

If students develop their own general rules about the relationship between sign and operation, such as "adding a negative gives the same result as subtracting a positive," that's fine. However, tell them that familiarity with the hot-and-cold-cube model will give them something to fall back on if they happen to forget the rule someday. If they don't come up with these catch phrases, that's also fine.

You can also mention that today they will see another method, based on patterns, for understanding some of these rules.

- *Using an initial temperature*

The hot-and-cold-cube model focuses on the *change* in temperature, rather than the final result. The sample explanation above for Question 4 looks only at the change. But some students may want or need to work with a starting temperature in order to see what the change is.

If they do, they may want to use a thermometer with a vertical number line, like the one illustrated, to trace the steps of their calculation.

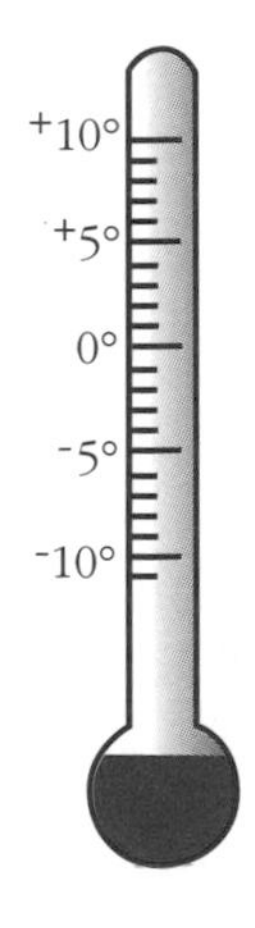

(A large copy of this diagram is included in Appendix B for your convenience in making an overhead transparency.)

For example, suppose that the problem is $^{+}5 + {}^{-}12$. If the initial temperature is 0°, the explanation could use a diagram like the one below, where you first go up from 0° to 5° and then go down from 5° to $^{-}7$°.

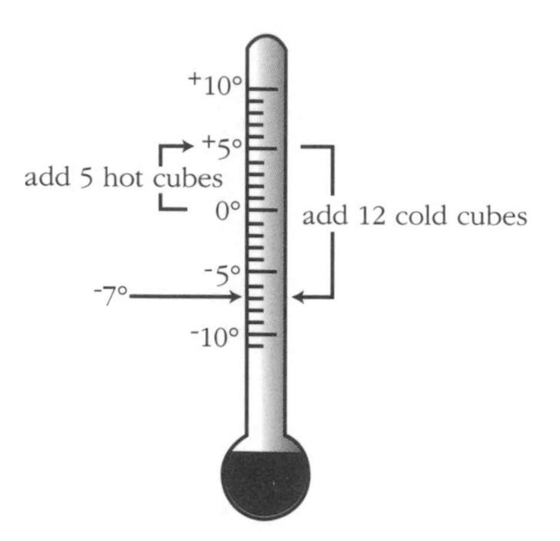

The net result is to change the temperature from 0° to $^{-}7$°, so that the temperature has gone down by 7°. This visual picture of operations with integers should be of help to some students, but be sure that they come back to the change itself and put the whole situation together to answer the original arithmetic question.

Students will probably realize that using 0° as the starting temperature means that the final temperature has the same numerical value as the net change, both in absolute value and in direction. In other words, they should see that the final temperature of $^{-}7$° corresponds to the fact that $^{+}5 + {}^{-}12 = {}^{-}7$.

Note: If students choose to use a starting temperature other than 0°, and can work successfully with that, that's fine.

- ***Standard notation and the use of parentheses for multiplication***

Tell students that from now on, you will generally omit the raised plus sign prefix for positive numbers and will write the negative sign the same way as a subtraction sign. Student materials make the same change at this point. This is also a good time to remind students that we often use parentheses to indicate multiplication. You can illustrate with an example such as 5(-3). Explain that this means 5 *times* -3, and not 5 - 3.

> *Note:* Students are probably familiar with parentheses to mean multiplication in expressions like 5(2 + 7), but may not have seen parentheses used in a context where there is a symbol immediately inside the parentheses that could be interpreted as an arithmetic operation.

Tell students also that we usually avoid writing two symbols next to each other, so we would not generally write 5 • -3, although we could write

$5 \cdot (-3)$. Similarly, we avoid expressions like $10 + -7$ or $8 - -4$, and instead insert parentheses, writing $10 + (-7)$ or $8 - (-4)$.

3. A Pattern Approach to Arithmetic of Integers

Whenever possible, we want to give students a variety of ways to model a problem. With this in mind, bring the class together to present an approach to operating with negative numbers that uses patterns. After working through the ideas below, you can informally connect this way of thinking about the arithmetic of integers to the theme and title of the unit, *Patterns*.

- ***Patterns with addition***

Begin by writing the following sequence of equations.

$$7 + 3 = 10$$

$$7 + 2 = 9$$

$$7 + 1 = 8$$

$$7 + 0 = 7$$

$$7 + (-1) = ?$$

"What should come next?"

Ask students to look for a pattern and explain what number goes in place of the question mark. Presumably they will see that the sequence of answers suggests that $7 + (-1)$ should equal 6.

Continue with $7 + (-2) = ?$ and similar problems. Ask students what is happening. They should see that as negative numbers of greater absolute value are added, the resulting sum gets smaller. Continue through $7 + (-7)$ and on into examples such as $7 + (-8)$ that give a negative sum.

After the pattern has been described, ask the class if this pattern gives the same answers as the hot-and-cold-cube model. Students should be able to explain how to get the same results from the model.

You can have students look at the problems $7 + (-1) = ?$, $7 + (-2) = ?$, $7 + (-3) = ?$, and so on, and ask them if there are similar problems that give the same results. Someone might see that there are related subtraction problems. If not, this discovery will probably come up at a later time.

- ***Patterns with subtraction***

The next series of equations relates to subtraction. Present the equations

$$7 - 5 = 2$$

$$7 - 6 = 1$$

$$7 - 7 = 0$$

$$7 - 8 = ?$$

"What should come next?"

From the continuation of this pattern, students should see that if a greater number is subtracted from a lesser number, the result will be a negative number. Furthermore, some students may notice that the result is the opposite of the result when the two numbers are reversed. Again, have them also do these problems in terms of the hot-and-cold-cube model.

Next, continue the pattern above in the opposite direction. That is, subtract smaller and smaller numbers from 7.

$$7 - 5 = 2$$

$$7 - 4 = 3$$

$$7 - 3 = 4$$

$$7 - 2 = 5$$

$$7 - 1 = 6$$

$$7 - 0 = 7$$

$$7 - (-1) = ?$$

"What should come next?"

From the continuation of this pattern, students should notice that, in general, as the number subtracted gets smaller, the result gets greater. More specifically, some students may see that subtracting a negative number gives the same result as adding the corresponding positive number, so that there is a related addition equation for each subtraction equation. For example, they may relate the subtraction equation $7 - (-5) = 12$ to the addition equation $7 + 5 = 12$.

- ***Patterns with multiplication***

Finally, have students look for a pattern for the product of integers, using a sequence of problems like the one given below.

$$6 \cdot 3 = 18$$

$$6 \cdot 2 = 12$$

$$6 \cdot 1 = 6$$

$$6 \cdot 0 = 0$$

$$6 \cdot (-1) = ?$$

"What should come next?"

Students should observe that as the second factor decreases by 1, the products decrease by 6. Therefore, to find the next entry, they would subtract 6 from 0 and get -6.

Homework 14 You're the Chef

After a lengthy term as "Number One Chef in the World," you have decided to step down and retire to the warmer climates of the Lazy Chef Sunset Ranch. It has been a memorable time, but one with many responsibilities.

Though it was fun to be a master chef, any drastic miscalculation of the temperature could have caused catastrophic results.

Your final responsibility before retirement is to train an assistant chef to take your place. Assistant chefs spend most of their time helping children with their homework, so they know very little about changing the temperature in the cauldron. But they do know how to do arithmetic with whole numbers.

Prepare a manual for the assistant chef who will be taking your place. Be sure to include specific examples of all the different ways to raise and lower the temperature.

Homework 14: You're the Chef

In the homework tonight students write instructions to an assistant chef about how to work the hot-and-cold-cube cauldron.

This assignment will be part of student portfolios for the unit. You may want to announce this to students.

Patterns

An Angle on Patterns

This page in the student book introduces Days 15 through 19.

Mathematics is not just about numbers. People long ago invented geometry to understand the physical space around them. (The word "geometry" comes from the Greek root words that mean "measuring the earth.")

A group of students uses pattern blocks to measure angles.

In the next few days of the unit, you'll explore angles and polygons, which are important building blocks of the geometric world. And speaking of blocks, you'll get to work with some objects called pattern blocks to help strengthen your understanding of the ideas.

You'll continue to work with In-Out tables and see how they can help you with the numerical aspects of geometry. You'll also continue the work with proof that you began in *Homework 2: Who's Who* and *Homework 12: That's Odd!*

DAY 15

POW 2 Presentations and Pattern Blocks

Students do POW presentations and also explore pattern blocks in preparation for using them in work with angles.

Mathematical Topics

- Summary of principles for working with integers
- Examining ways to create numerical expressions with given values
- Introduction of pattern blocks as a tool for exploring geometric concepts
- Introduction of terminology related to polygons

Outline of the Day

In Class

1. Discuss *Homework 14: You're the Chef*
2. Presentations of *POW 2: 1-2-3-4 Puzzle*
   - Focus on how students found their expressions
3. *Pattern Block Designs*
   - Students are introduced to pattern blocks and explore how they fit together
   - Introduce the terms **triangle**, **hexagon**, **rhombus**, **square**, **trapezoid**, **polygon**, and **quadrilateral**
   - No whole-class discussion of this activity is needed

At Home

Homework 15: Rules, Rules, Rules

POW 3: Checkerboard Squares (due Day 21)

Special Materials Needed

- About half a tub of pattern blocks for each group

1. Discussion of *Homework 14: You're the Chef*

Have a few students read their papers to the class. We suggest that you collect this assignment for grading. Even if you choose not to grade it, you may want to read some of the papers to get a sense of how well students have understood the use of the model.

As an alternative, rather than collect the assignment now, you may want to discuss the ideas and then let students redo their work and turn in revised versions tomorrow.

Note: A supplemental problem, *Chef Divisions,* asks students to develop ways to interpret division problems in terms of the hot-and-cold-cube model.

2. Presentations of *POW 2: 1-2-3-4 Puzzle*

As needed, review the general guidelines about presentations discussed on Days 3 and 9, and have the students selected yesterday present their work on the POW to the whole class. Have presenters pay particular attention to describing *how* they found their 1-2-3-4 expressions.

- Did they proceed in numerical order or did they jump around?
- Did they get an expression for one number by adjusting their expression for another?
- Did they use any patterns that they saw in the expressions?

"Does anyone have anything to add to the presentations?"

After the presentations, ask if other students have ideas to add: other patterns, extensions, variations of the problem, and so forth.

• *Is this mathematics?*

"Is this POW mathematics or is it arithmetic?"

This is an opportunity to make the *evaluation* component of the POW write-up more meaningful for students. You can pose the following question to the class.

> *Would you describe working on this problem as doing* mathematics *or doing* arithmetic*?*

Let students share their ideas and perspectives. Encourage them to share parts of their work where they went beyond simple calculation and used some reasoning to assist the process.

Suggest to students that they address issues like the "mathematics versus arithmetic" question when they evaluate a POW.

3. *Pattern Block Designs*

(see next page)

Over the course of the next several days, students will learn about the concept of angle. *Pattern Block Designs* introduces students to pattern blocks—a manipulative tool that they will use in the development of this concept.

When students encounter a new manipulative material, they often need time to explore its properties and possibilities. You can begin by giving students the blocks and allowing them a few minutes of free play. As they play with the blocks, introduce the name **pattern blocks** for the set of materials. You can informally connect this name to the theme and title of the unit, *Patterns*.

Introduce names for the different blocks—**triangle**, **hexagon**, **rhombus** (or *diamond*), **square**, and **trapezoid**. You can refer to the two different rhombi either by shape (*wide* and *thin*) or by color (*blue* and *tan*).

Also introduce the general term **polygon** and the term **quadrilateral** for any four-sided polygon.

Note: You may want to remind students to take notes as needed on this terminology.

After the free play, have students work on *Pattern Block Designs,* which is primarily an opportunity to continue the informal exploration of the pattern blocks.

After a short time (at most, ten minutes) on Question 1, have students turn to Question 2.

Students will probably see that four squares fit together, three hexagons fit together, and six triangles fit together. If they don't see that the other three blocks can also be used, you can mention to them as they explore that they haven't yet gotten all the possibilities.

Whatever cases they do find, you can point out that these blocks at least *appear* to fit together, but that students can't be sure yet whether they actually fit together perfectly, or just come very close.

There is no need for a general discussion of this activity, although you may want to discuss ways that students fit different blocks together.

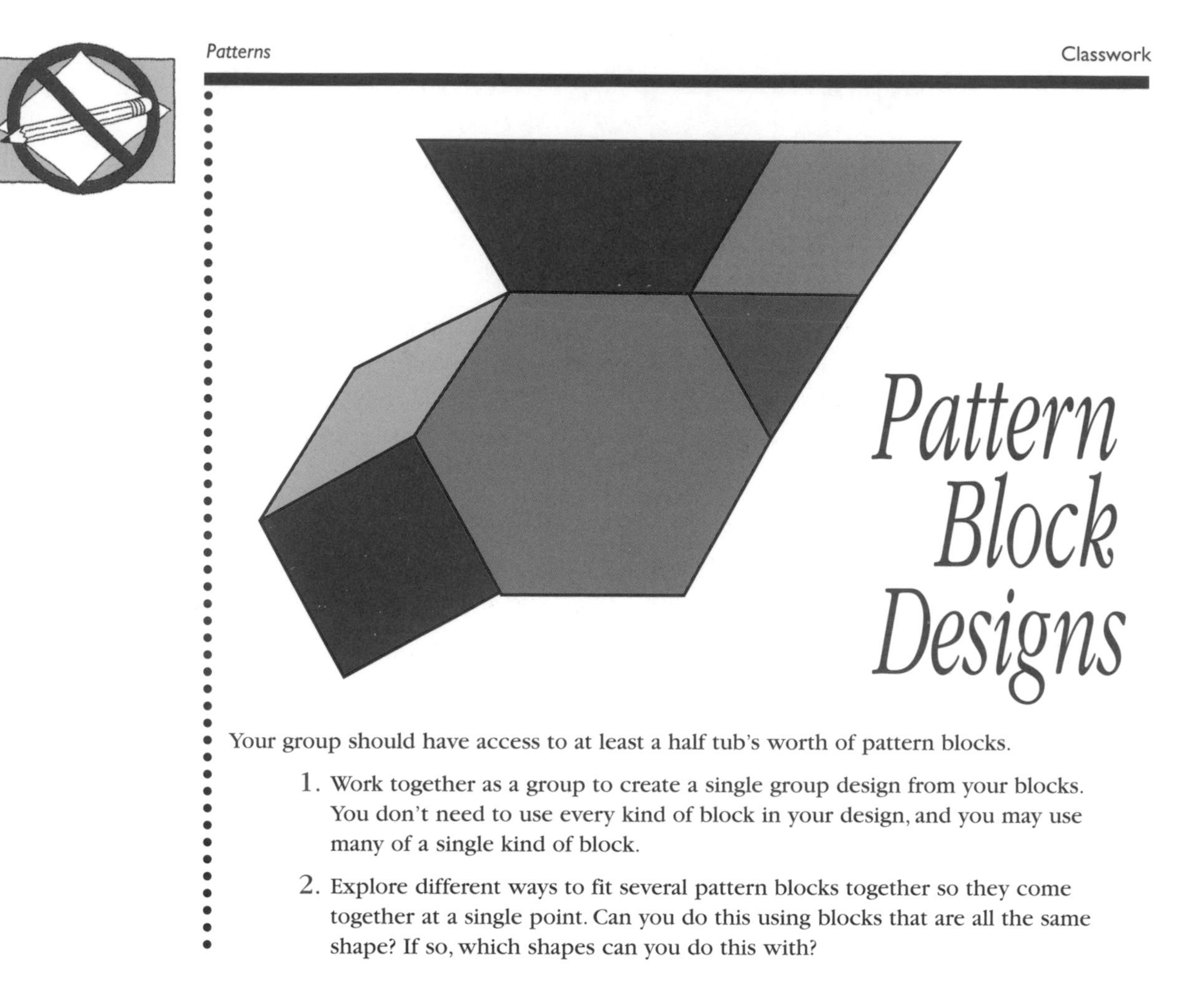

Pattern Block Designs

Your group should have access to at least a half tub's worth of pattern blocks.

1. Work together as a group to create a single group design from your blocks. You don't need to use every kind of block in your design, and you may use many of a single kind of block.

2. Explore different ways to fit several pattern blocks together so they come together at a single point. Can you do this using blocks that are all the same shape? If so, which shapes can you do this with?

Homework 15 Rules, Rules, Rules

1. There are many rules that fit the information in the In-Out table at the right.

   Your task is to find at least ten different rules that work. You can use multiplication, division, addition, subtraction, and exponents, and you can use more than one operation in a single rule.

In	Out
5	16

2. The table at the right gives a bit more information than the one above, but that just makes things harder.

   Find as many rules as you can that fit both rows of this table.

In	Out
1	2
2	5

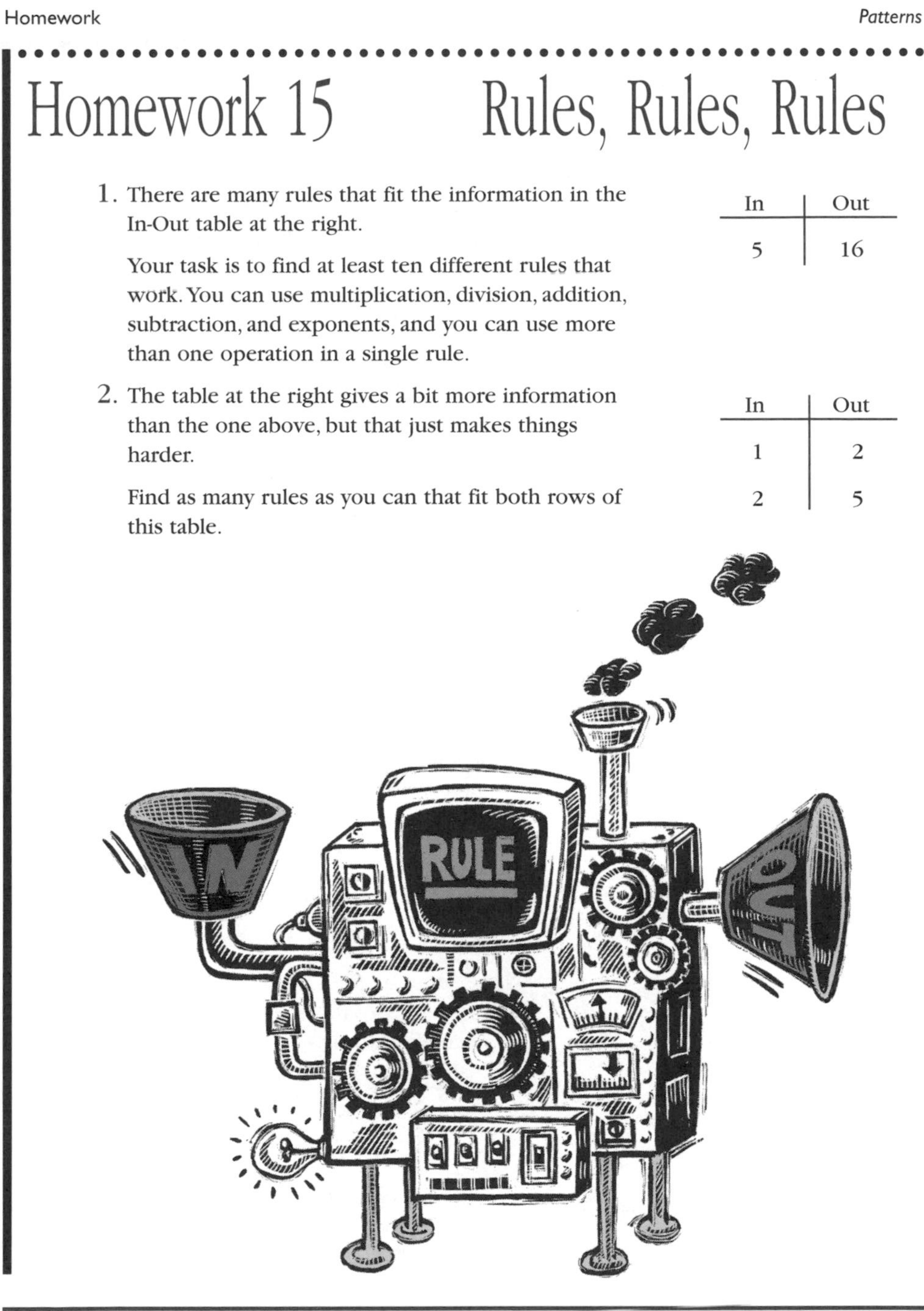

Homework 15: Rules, Rules, Rules

The homework problems continue to work with the idea presented in Question 2 of ***Homework 10: Pulling Out Rules***.

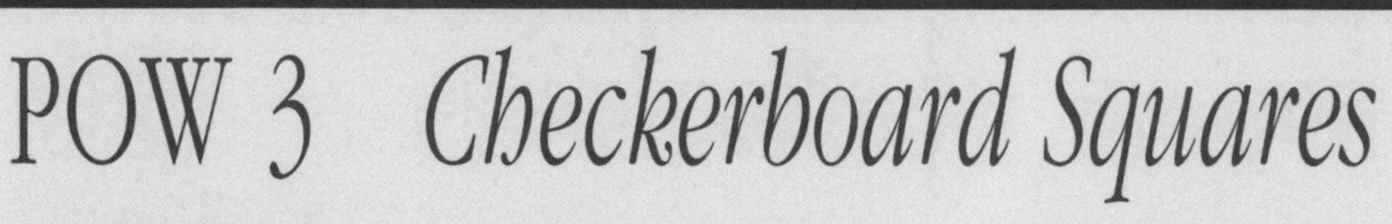

POW 3 Checkerboard Squares

The picture at the left shows a standard 8-by-8 checkerboard, made up of 64 small squares.

But there are many other squares of various sizes within the checkerboard.

For example, the diagram at the right shows a 3-by-3 square outlined within the larger checkerboard. (This is just one of many 3-by-3 squares.)

The first question of this POW is this:

1. How many squares are there altogether on the checkerboard?

When you are confident that you have counted all the squares of various sizes on the 8-by-8 checkerboard, move on to the generalization.

2. Suppose you have a square checkerboard of some other size—not 8-by-8. How can you determine how many squares are on it altogether?

   You will know you are done with this problem when you feel confident that, no matter what size checkerboard you are given, you can quickly and easily compute the total number of squares.

Write-up

1. *Problem Statement*
2. *Process:* Be sure to describe any diagrams or materials you used.
3. *Solution:* Explain your answer in the case of the 8-by-8 checkerboard in complete detail. Also give results, with explanations, on any other specific checkerboard sizes you studied. Be sure to include your reasoning in discussing any generalizations you found.
4. *Extensions*
5. *Evaluation*

POW 3: Checkerboard Squares

Introduce the unit's third Problem of the Week. You may want to point out the 3×3 square shown in the diagram to be sure that students understand that squares of all sizes should be considered.

On Day 20, students will read each other's POWs and discuss what makes a good POW write-up. The presentations of this POW are scheduled for Day 21.

DAY 16

Investigation of Angles

Students look at the concept of angle both as a turn and as a geometric figure.

Mathematical Topics

- Finding several rules for partial In-Out tables
- Introduction to angles both as turns and as geometric figures
- Degree measurement
- Angle of a polygon
- Using pattern blocks to find the angles of certain polygons

Outline of the Day

In Class

1. Remind students that they will need protractors tomorrow
2. Discuss *Homework 15: Rules, Rules, Rules*
3. Introduce angles as turns
   - Define degree measurement
   - Introduce the terms **right angle**, **acute angle, obtuse angle**
4. Introduce angles as geometric figures
   - Introduce the terms **vertex**, **side of an angle, ray**
   - Define angle of a polygon
   - Introduce the terms **vertex** and **side** as applied to polygons
5. *Pattern Block Angles*
   - Students use pattern blocks to find the angles of certain polygons
6. Discuss *Pattern Block Angles*
   - Have students share results
   - Post the angles of pattern blocks for reference

At Home

Homework 16: Another In-Outer

Special Materials Needed

- About half a tub of pattern blocks for each group
- (Optional) A set of pattern blocks designed for use on an overhead projector

1. Reminder on Protractors

Students will need protractors tomorrow. Although they were told to get them on Day 1, you may want to warn students that they will definitely need their protractors tomorrow.

2. Discussion of *Homework 15: Rules, Rules, Rules*

You can have group members share with each other the rules that they found on each question. Then begin with Question 1 and have the spade card member of each group share one of the group's rules with the whole class. Keep going around from group to group until you have a long list of rules.

Question 2 is a greater challenge. If students had trouble coming up with more than one rule for the table, you might want to give them a few minutes to brainstorm possibilities. Having students come up with more answers is not as important as encouraging them to experiment. (As a hint, you might suggest that they use exponents.)

"How can this type of activity help with your work on In-Out tables and on problem solving?"

To sum up, ask students how questions like those in the homework can help them in their work with In-Out tables and with problem solving. Help them see that one approach to finding a rule for a table or situation is to experiment with lots of possibilities and then test them against the given data.

3. Angles as Turns

The main subject for today is the concept of **angle.** Angles can be thought of in different ways, and today's lesson looks at them from two perspectives. One perspective is dynamic, in which we think of an angle as a turn. The other is static, in which we think of an angle as a geometric figure.

For most students, the dynamic concept of an angle as a turn is an easier place to start.

"How far have I turned?"

Begin by demonstrating a complete turn (360 degrees). Stand facing the class, make a complete turn, and ask the class, "How far have I turned?" The discussion should include the fact that you have not traveled any distance and therefore the traditional measures of length are inappropriate for measuring a turn.

Some students may express their answer by saying that you have turned "one complete turn." Others may be familiar with degree measurement and say that you have turned 360 degrees. Let students know that both answers are correct, and that a **degree** is the name for a turn that is $\frac{1}{360}$ of a complete turn. Use the symbol for degrees; for example, write "360°" for the complete turn.

Tell the class that a degree is just one possible unit for measuring angles, but it is the most commonly used unit, and it is the one they will be using throughout the IMP curriculum. (In Year 4, students will be introduced to radian measure, but will not do significant work with it.)

You can tell students that the division of the complete turn into 360 equal parts is quite ancient and is often attributed to the Babylonians, whose number system was based on 60 and for whom the number 360 played an important role.

"How many degrees in that turn?"

Then have students demonstrate some other turns. For example, ask all club card students to stand and do a half turn, and then ask the rest of the class to figure out how many degrees the turn is. Then have diamond card students do some other fraction of a turn.

Note: All the students might not turn in the same direction. In some contexts, it's important to use counterclockwise turns for positive angles, but that isn't necessary in this introductory work. If students find the use of both directions confusing, let them choose a common direction for their turns.

"Can you turn 120°?"

Also go from degrees to turns. For example, ask heart card students to turn 120°, and ask the class to describe what fraction of a whole turn that is. Then have spade card students do some other turn. Most students need to develop a physical feeling for the turning concept, and this approach lets everyone get involved both physically and mentally.

Note: Use your judgment about whether or not to consider the case of turns greater than 360° at this point.

Also emphasize that, when in doubt, students should go back to the fact that a complete turn is 360°. They can always use this frame of reference to go from a fraction of a turn to degrees or vice versa.

Ask if anyone knows the special name for a quarter turn. If not, introduce the term **right angle** and have students figure out how many degrees it must be.

Also, tell students that an angle between 0° and 90° is called an **acute angle** (be careful that students don't think you're calling it "a cute angle") and that an angle between 90° and 180° is called an **obtuse angle**.

4. Angles as Geometric Figures

Another important way to think about an angle is as a geometric figure (or part of one).

"Where is the angle in this diagram?"

Show students a diagram such as that below, and ask them where the angle is in the diagram.

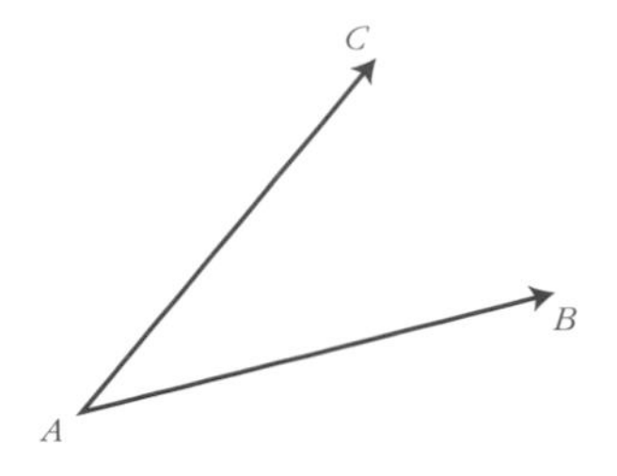

As needed, explain that in order to think of this diagram as showing an angle in the sense of a turn, they should imagine standing at A and facing toward B, and then imagine turning toward C (while continuing to stand at A).

You may find it very helpful to lay out a diagram like this on the floor (for example, with two pieces of tape), so that students can connect it with their physical sense of angle, as developed earlier. Have a student stand at the vertex, first looking along one piece of tape and then turning to look along the other.

Extend the lengths of the sides of the angle and ask students how this changes the angle itself. Many students confuse the lengths of the sides with the size of the angle, so it is important to bring out early and often that the angle itself remains unchanged. This understanding will be crucial when students learn to use protractors.

Tell students that point A is called the **vertex** of the angle and that the segments from A to B and from A to C are called the **sides** of the angle. (You can mention that the extensions of these segments through B or C are called **rays**.) Also introduce the notation $\angle BAC$ (read as *angle BAC*).

Tell students that if there's no chance of confusion, such an angle can be referred to simply as $\angle A$. You may want to point out that confusion could arise in a more complex diagram such as one that has several lines through A.

You can mention that if we start by facing C and then turn toward B (rather than vice versa), we would probably refer to the angle as $\angle CAB$.

Make it clear that whether we start facing B or facing C, we generally assume that we turn "the short way." Thus, in the diagram above, if we start at A facing toward B, we would turn **counterclockwise** in order to face C, rather than make almost a whole turn clockwise.

• *Angle of a polygon*

For the next activity, *Pattern Block Angles*, students will also need to be familiar with the concept of an **angle of a polygon.** (The term *polygon* should have been introduced yesterday.)

You can introduce the concept by drawing any polygon. You may need to begin with the terminology of **side** and **vertex** as applied to a polygon, and to introduce the plural *vertices* as well.

Then ask students to identify the angles of the polygon. Explain, if needed, that an angle of a polygon is an angle formed where two sides of a polygon meet at a vertex. Thus, a polygon has the same number of angles as it has vertices (which is also the same as the number of its sides).

Use the special case of a square or rectangle to illustrate this fact, and ask students to find the sizes of the angles of such a figure. They should be able to connect this question with the earlier discussion and see that each angle is a quarter turn, so all the angles are 90°.

5. *Pattern Block Angles*

(see next page)

After introducing students to angles, have them begin the activity *Pattern Block Angles*. Tell students they should do this activity by working only with the blocks themselves. Circulate as they work, giving hints if needed, such as suggesting that students think about fitting blocks together to make complete turns. (See photo on page 151.)

- *Overview for teachers: Angle sums and proof*

Pattern Block Angles is the first of several activities in this unit involving angles and angle sums for polygons. In this activity, students look at the way pattern blocks fit together and are asked to think of the angles of the blocks as fractions of a complete turn. Then they express the angles in degrees.

In the Day 18 activity, *Degree Discovery*, they will look at general triangles and quadrilaterals.

Through these two activities, students should observe that the angle sum for a triangle always seems to be 180° and that the angle sum for a quadrilateral always seems to be 360°. They will probably observe similar facts about polygons in general in *Homework 18: Polygon Angles.*

It is important for students to recognize that these observations are based on experimentation, measurement, and estimation, and on a limited set of examples. Persuasive as this evidence may be, it is not a proof.

On Day 19, students will be asked to prove that *if* every triangle has an angle sum of 180°, *then* every quadrilateral has an angle sum of 360° (and justify similar facts for polygons with more sides). This type of logic is both powerful and sophisticated, allowing students to see a chain of ideas and to focus on the connection from one to the next. Appreciation of this logic depends in part on students realizing the conjectural nature of the conclusions they reached based on measurement.

Students will leave *Patterns* with their formulas for polygon angle sums still at the level of conjecture, but knowing that if they can prove the formula for triangles, the rest must follow.

In the *Shadows* unit, later in Year 1, students will further investigate the topic of angle sums. At that time, they will prove that the angle sum for a triangle is always exactly 180°, thus filling in the missing first step that completes the proof for all polygons.

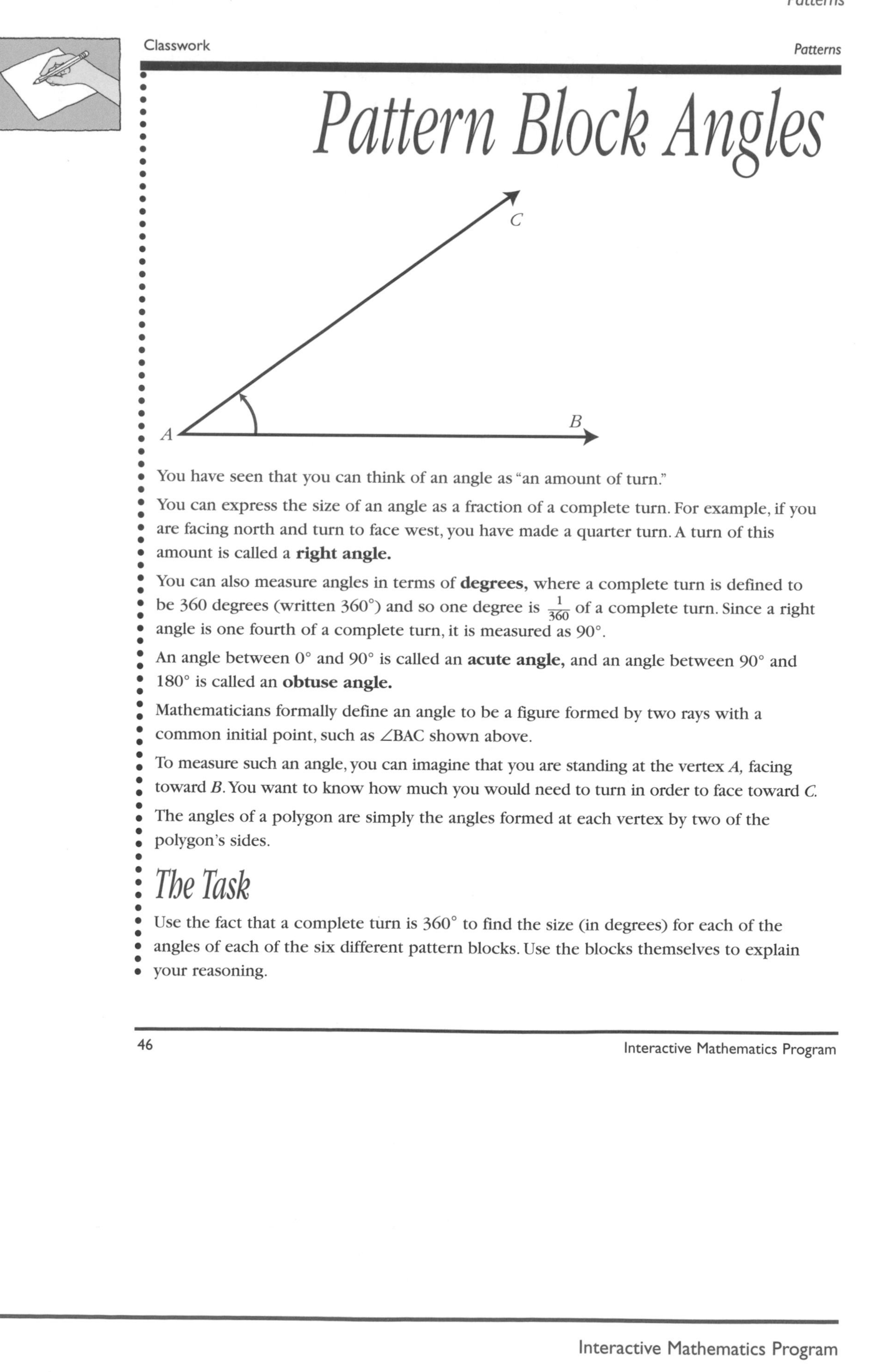

Pattern Block Angles

You have seen that you can think of an angle as "an amount of turn."

You can express the size of an angle as a fraction of a complete turn. For example, if you are facing north and turn to face west, you have made a quarter turn. A turn of this amount is called a **right angle.**

You can also measure angles in terms of **degrees,** where a complete turn is defined to be 360 degrees (written 360°) and so one degree is $\frac{1}{360}$ of a complete turn. Since a right angle is one fourth of a complete turn, it is measured as 90°.

An angle between 0° and 90° is called an **acute angle,** and an angle between 90° and 180° is called an **obtuse angle.**

Mathematicians formally define an angle to be a figure formed by two rays with a common initial point, such as ∠BAC shown above.

To measure such an angle, you can imagine that you are standing at the vertex *A,* facing toward *B*. You want to know how much you would need to turn in order to face toward *C.*

The angles of a polygon are simply the angles formed at each vertex by two of the polygon's sides.

The Task

Use the fact that a complete turn is 360° to find the size (in degrees) for each of the angles of each of the six different pattern blocks. Use the blocks themselves to explain your reasoning.

6. Discussion of *Pattern Block Angles*

"How did you figure out the size of that angle?"

If students worked successfully on this, they should have found all of the individual angles.

You can ask for one or two explanations. (If you have pattern blocks for the overhead projector, they will be useful here.)

Most of these explanations should be straightforward, such as "I could fit six triangles together at a single point, so each angle is a sixth of a turn, which is 60°."

Students will need to do something more subtle in order to find the large angle of the thin rhombus, such as fit it together with a right angle from a square and an angle from the hexagon.

As you did yesterday, bring out that these angle measurements are based on the assumption that blocks are fitting together *perfectly*. For instance, you can suggest that the angles of the triangle block might really be 59.8° and only seem to fit together.

POST THIS

Post the results from this activity for later reference, perhaps with a poster showing the blocks and each of their angles.

Mike Duva explains his solution to "Homework 16: Another In-Outer."

Homework 16 Another In-Outer

Find the missing items in each of the following In-Out machines.

In Questions 1, 4, and 5, give a description in words for how to find the *Out* from the *In*.

In Questions 2, 3, and 6, give an algebraic expression for the *Out* as a function of the *In*.

1.

In	Out
●	LBC
○	SWC
■	LBS
△	SWT
□	?
?	LWT

2.

In	Out
2	-6
5	-15
0	0
13	?
-7	?
?	-30
?	35

3.

In	Out
1	5
3	11
7	23
10	32
-2	-4
-5	?
?	2
?	-19

4.

In	Out
Ruth	U
Johnny	I
Carol	S
Anne	O
Aaron	S
Robert	?

Continued on next page

Homework 16: Another In-Outer

This homework provides more practice in finding patterns and in expressing rules algebraically. This assignment contains the first appearance of the word *function* in the student materials, and it includes the first use of negative numbers in In-Out tables.

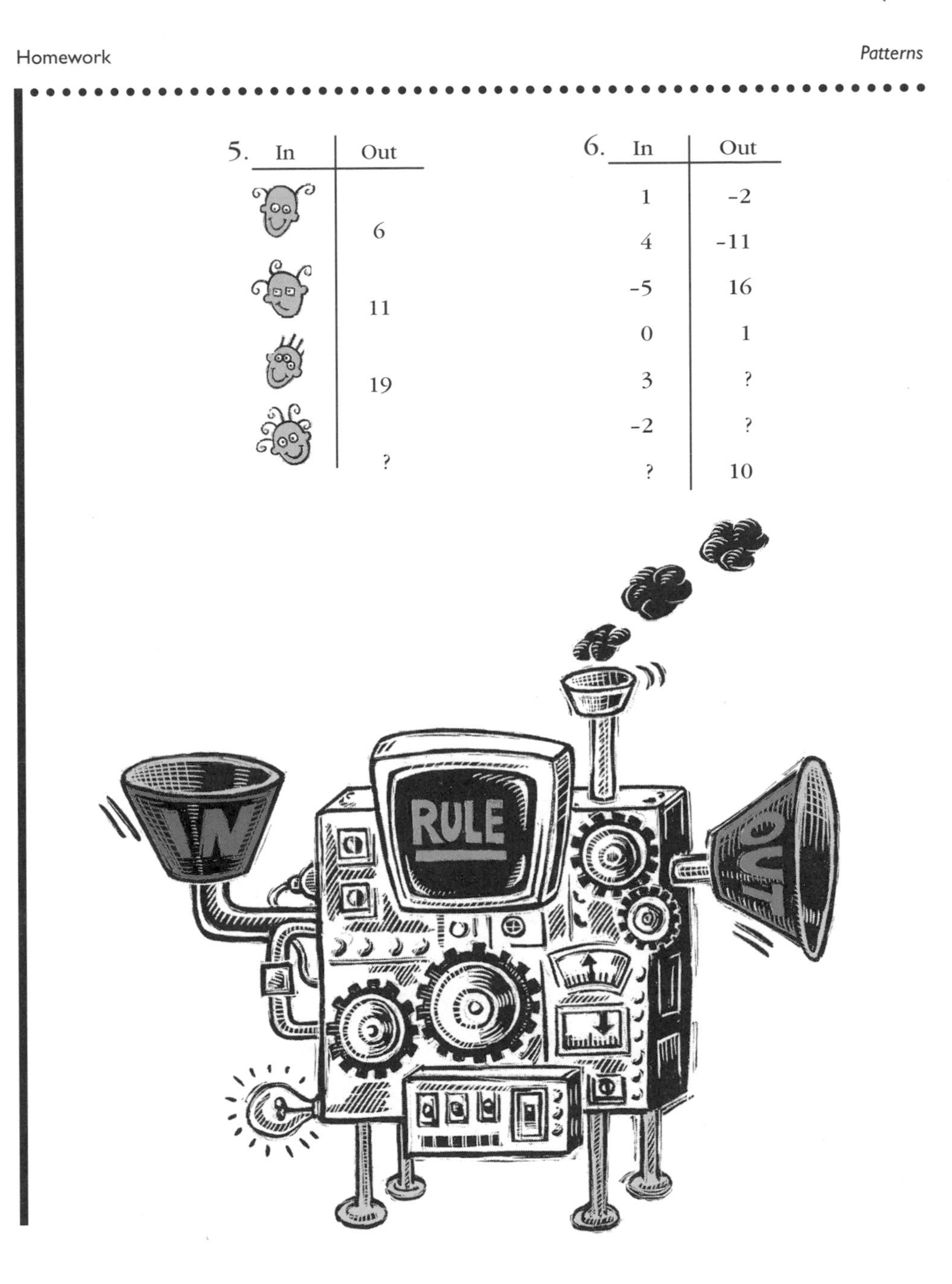

5.

In	Out
	6
	11
	19
	?

6.

In	Out
1	-2
4	-11
-5	16
0	1
3	?
-2	?
?	10

Day 17 Protractors

Students learn about protractors and use them to decode a message.

Mathematical Topics

- Finding rules for numerical and nonnumerical In-Out tables
- Using protractors

Outline of the Day

In Class

1. Remind students to be working on *POW 3: Checkerboard Squares*
2. Discuss *Homework 16: Another In-Outer*
3. Introduce the use of protractors
4. *A Protracted Engagement*
   - Students decode a message by measuring angles
   - No whole-class discussion of this activity is needed

At Home

Homework 17: Diagonally Speaking

Special Materials Needed

- Clear plastic protractor for use at the overhead projector

1. *POW 3: Checkerboard Squares*—Reminder for Students

Remind students that they should be working on *POW 3: Checkerboard Squares*. By now they probably have found the number of squares for the 8×8 checkerboard and should be considering the general problem. If they are stuck, you may want to suggest that they work on a simpler problem first, such as a 3×3 or 4×4 checkerboard.

You may want to consider giving them the numerical answer for the case of the 8×8 checkerboard (the answer is 204) in order to focus students on the importance of *explanation* in their POW work.

2. Discussion of *Homework 16: Another In-Outer*

You can have the club card members of different groups each report on one of the In-Out tables from the homework.

Use Questions 2, 3, and 6 to uncover any confusion or questions about the arithmetic of integers. Use the last example in Question 2 as a brief introduction to negative numbers other than integers. That is, tell students that every positive number has an opposite, and that the arithmetic of positive and negative numbers in general is defined using the same principles as those used for integers.

Be aware that the use of mixed numbers for negative numbers is potentially confusing, especially because we read them with an "and," which might mean "plus." You may want to clarify, for example, that $-11\frac{2}{3}$ does not mean $-11 + \frac{2}{3}$.

Students may be confused, in Question 3, by the fact that some outputs appear to be "more than" three times the input while others appear to be "less than" three times the input. (The same thing happens in Question 6.) If this confusion arises, use it as an opportunity to review the idea of absolute value as well as the number line meaning of "greater than" and "less than."

The most engaging example from the homework is probably Question 5 (the one with the funny faces). Here are two possible rules.

- 3(number of eyes) + 5(number of hairs) − 10
- (number of hairs)^2 + number of eyes

Both of these formulas fit all three rows that are given in the table, but the first formula gives 21 for the missing entry, while the second gives 27.

If students were stuck on this one, you might suggest making an In-Out table showing the number of eyes and the number of hairs both as *Ins*, using the given *Out* column. Such a table might look like the one below.

In		*Out*
Number of eyes	Number of hairs	
2	2	6
2	3	11
3	4	19
2	5	?

Finding a rule for this table can be left as an open problem.

3. Protractors

Explain to the class how to use a protractor. This is a difficult tool for many students to learn to use, and today's lesson is devoted to getting students comfortable with it. The use of a clear plastic protractor on the overhead projector can be very helpful to your demonstration.

"What point on the protractor corresponds to the vertex of the angle?"

Instruction on using the protractor should build on the perspective emphasized yesterday in which angles are viewed primarily as partial turns. You can begin by having students identify the special point on their protractors that corresponds to the vertex of the angle. For clarity, we will refer to this point as the *vertex* of the protractor, although this is not standard terminology.

Have students draw an angle and place the protractor so that its vertex is at the vertex of the angle.

Next, ask them to maneuver the protractor so that one side of the angle (extended if necessary) goes through a point on the protractor marked 0°. Be sure that they continue to keep the vertex of the protractor on the vertex of the angle.

Show students that the protractor has two points marked 0°, and ask students how they should decide which one to use. Essentially their choice depends on which direction they are turning. They should place the protractor so that the starting side of the angle goes through that point marked 0° which makes the numbers on the scale increase from 0° in the same direction as the turn of the angle.

Once they have the protractor correctly positioned, discuss how to read the amount of the turn from the proper scale.

Urge students to estimate the angles they are measuring as a way of checking the reasonableness of their answers. For example, they should be able to visually identify an angle between 0° to 180° as either *acute* (between 0° and 90°), *right* (equal to 90°), or *obtuse* (between 90° and 180°). (*Note:* Angles very close to 90° may be difficult to characterize.) Similarly, they should also be able to visually categorize an acute angle as either less than 45°, about 45°, or between 45° and 90°.

"What can you do if the sides of the angle don't reach the edge of the protractor?"

You will probably need to pay special attention to the situation where the sides of the angle do not reach to the edge of the protractor. Ask the class what to do about that. They should see that it's all right to extend the sides as far as needed. Discussion of this issue should reinforce the concept that when one measures an angle, one is measuring *the amount of turn* and not the lengths of the sides that form it.

A Protracted Engagement

Deon and Marsha thought of an interesting way to announce their long-awaited wedding.

They decided to send the invitations out in code. In the code they decided on, each letter is represented by an angle of a certain size.

An angle between 0° and 5° represents the letter *A*, an angle between 5° and 10° represents *B*, an angle between 10° and 15° represents *C*, and so on.

To avoid confusion, they never used angles that were exact multiples of 5°. The design below spells out part of their invitation.

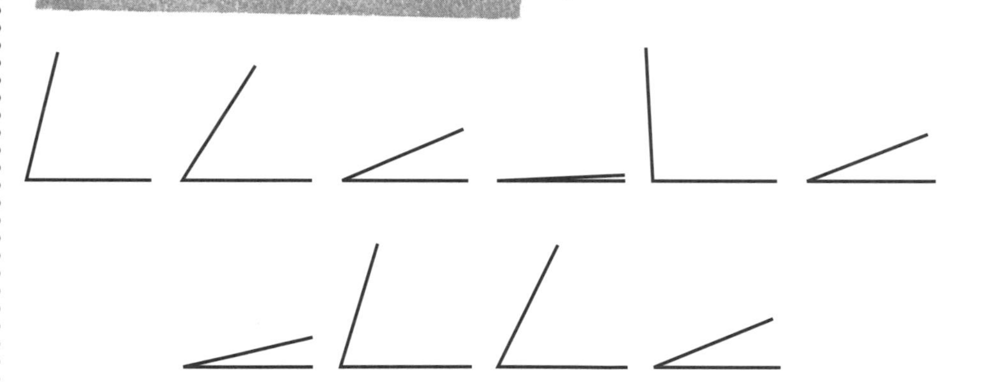

1. What does this message say?
2. Make up a message of your own that is between 10 and 20 letters long. You and other students can exchange and decipher each other's messages.

4. A Protracted Engagement

This activity provides a lighthearted context in which students can practice using a protractor. They can work on this activity in groups, and you probably do not need to involve the whole class in a discussion. You can circulate as students work on this activity to see if any students need further help or discussion on the use of protractors.

Homework 17 Diagonally Speaking

How many diagonals does a polygon have?

A **diagonal** is a line segment that connects two vertices of a polygon but is not a side of the polygon. For example, in the diagram at the right, segment AC is a diagonal and segment CD is a side of the polygon.

The diagram shows all the diagonals as dotted lines, and this polygon has five diagonals.

A B E C D

As you might expect, the number of diagonals in a polygon depends on the number of sides it has (which is the same as the number of vertices it has).

1. Experiment by drawing various polygons and finding out how many diagonals each has. Organize the results in an In-Out table in which the *In* is the number of sides of the polygon and the *Out* is the number of diagonals.

2. a. Look for a pattern for your In-Out table.

   b. Once you have found a pattern, use it to figure out how many diagonals a 12-sided polygon has. Try to confirm your result by actually counting the diagonals.

3. Think about *why* your pattern holds. That is, why should the number of diagonals in a polygon follow this pattern? Write down any explanations you come up with.

Homework 17: Diagonally Speaking

This problem provides an example of how the use of an In-Out table can give insight into a problem in geometry.

DAY 18 Degree Discovery

Students begin exploring angle sums for polygons.

Mathematical Topics

- Finding a pattern for the number of diagonals in a polygon in terms of the number of sides
- Exploring angle sums for triangles and quadrilaterals

Outline of the Day

In Class

1. Discuss *Homework 17: Diagonally Speaking*
   - Focus on getting each output from the previous output
   - (Optional) Introduce the concept of a **recursive function**
2. *Degree Discovery*
   - Students explore angle sums for triangles and quadrilaterals
3. Discuss *Degree Discovery*
   - Students should see that the angle sum for a triangle seems to be about 180° and that the angle sum for a quadrilateral seems to be about 360°
   - Articulate the distinction between experimental observation and proof

At Home

Homework 18: Polygon Angles

Special Materials Needed

- (Optional) Paper and scissors for making triangles

1. Discussion of *Homework 17: Diagonally Speaking*

You can call on several diamond card students to give you values to enter into an In-Out table, in which the *In* is the number of sides of a polygon and the *Out* is the number of diagonals. The table will probably look something like the one below. (Students might not bother with the first row, which is for triangles.)

Number of sides	Number of diagonals
3	0
4	2
5	5
6	9
7	14

Once students have gathered the data, ask for volunteers to describe patterns they found. Students probably will have seen the pattern by which each entry is obtained from the previous one. That is, they will have noticed that the number of diagonals goes up by 2, then by 3, then by 4, and so forth, as the number of sides goes up by 1 with each row of the table.

If they did not see this, it may be because they did not organize the table entries sequentially. In that case, you can have them reorganize their information as above, and look again for a pattern in the entries.

Even if students cannot articulate the pattern clearly, they probably will be able to use the pattern to find additional entries. By successive addition, they should be able to find that a 12-sided polygon has 54 diagonals—a result that they might have trouble obtaining by counting the diagonals in a diagram.

To follow up on their understanding of the pattern, you might say, for example, that a 20-sided polygon has 170 diagonals, and ask if anyone can tell you from that information how many diagonals a 21-sided polygon has. You can tell them that a rule which tells how to get an *Out* value from the previous *Out* value is called a **recursive function**.

- *Optional: Expressing the result as a sum*

Some students may describe how to find a given entry as a sum. For example, they may see that the number of diagonals in a 12-sided polygon is the sum $2 + 3 + \cdots + 10$. They may even express this using summation notation.

But you should not push the use of summation notation, and it is definitely *not* the intent that students here find a closed formula for the number of diagonals as a function of the number of sides; that is, do not press for an algebraic rule for the table above. (A supplemental problem, *Diagonals Illuminated,* provides an opportunity for students who want to look for such an algebraic expression.)

- *Explaining the pattern*

Ask students what explanations they found for the way the entries in the table increase. You can make this question more specific by asking, for example, why a 7-sided polygon should have five diagonals more than a 6-sided polygon, or why a 12-sided polygon should have ten diagonals more than a 11-sided polygon.

If students do not see a clear reason for this, you need not pursue it. But you can point out that without such an explanation, they can't be sure that the pattern they found in the table will continue for higher numbers of sides.

The supplemental problem *Diagonals Illuminated* also offers an opportunity for students to look for an explanation for this pattern.

2. *Degree Discovery*

(see next page)

Students can work on this activity in pairs or in their groups. It will give them additional practice with protractors and get them started on the important problem of analyzing the sum of the angles of a polygon.

Keep in mind that many students may still be having trouble using protractors.

3. Discussion of *Degree Discovery*

- ***Question 1***

First let students share their observations about triangles, in Question 1. Since they will be using approximate measurements, their angle sums may not be exactly 180°. But they should see that regardless of the shape of the triangle, the angles of a triangle always seems to add up to *about* 180°.

Some students may suggest that the angle sum for every triangle is exactly 180°, perhaps using their analysis in *Pattern Block Angles* (Day 16) for the triangle pattern block as support. (They should have seen in that activity that six triangle blocks seem to fit together around a single point, so the angles are apparently 60° each. As noted in the discussion for *Pattern Block Angles,* this is not a conclusive argument, since students have no way yet to be sure that the blocks fit together perfectly.)

Use the word *conjecture* to describe the suggestion that the angle sum for every triangle is 180°, and have students discuss what their "level of belief" is about this conjecture.

Probably some students will be skeptical. You can keep the level of skepticism high by asking whether everyone got this exact result for every triangle they measured. Even if they did, some may wonder whether the conjecture holds for *all* triangles. Be sure that these sources of doubt emerge, mentioning them yourself if necessary. You can use this discussion to review the term *counterexample*.

Degree Discovery

In the activity *Pattern Block Angles*, you found the angles of some very special polygons. In this activity, you will use protractors to explore more general polygons and also to look at the sum of the angles.

1. Begin with triangles. Use a ruler or straightedge to draw a variety of triangles, and measure the angles for each triangle. Then find the sum of the angles for each of your triangles.

   What conclusion do your results suggest? Does this conclusion hold for the angles you found for the triangle pattern block?

2. Now do the same for quadrilaterals. Does your conclusion hold for the angles you found for the various quadrilateral pattern blocks?

Note: As part of tomorrow's discussion of tonight's homework, students will be told that the angle sum for triangles *is* always 180° and that they will see a proof of this in a later Year 1 unit, *Shadows*. For now, you can leave this issue unresolved, so that students are not yet certain whether their conjecture is true.

- *Optional: A paper-cutting demonstration*

The following demonstration is another way to suggest that the sum of the angles of a triangle appears to be 180°. This method avoids the use of a protractor and can be done by students in pairs.

Cut out a paper triangle. Then number the angles and draw an arrow pointing at each vertex, as shown below. (The numbers and arrows will help keep track of what's going on when the triangle is cut.)

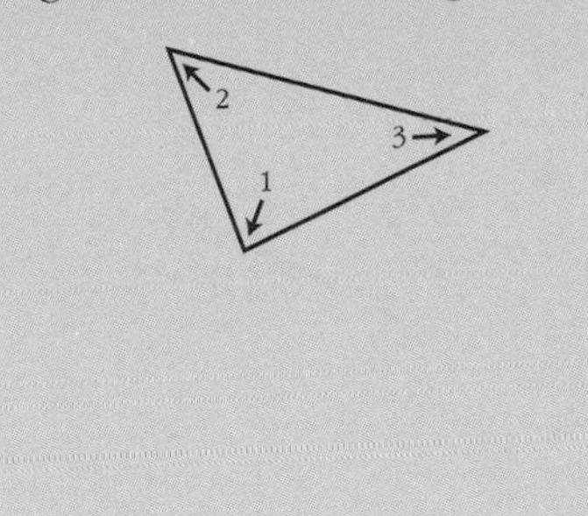

Next, tear the vertices off the paper triangle, and assemble the angles to form a straight angle, as shown below.

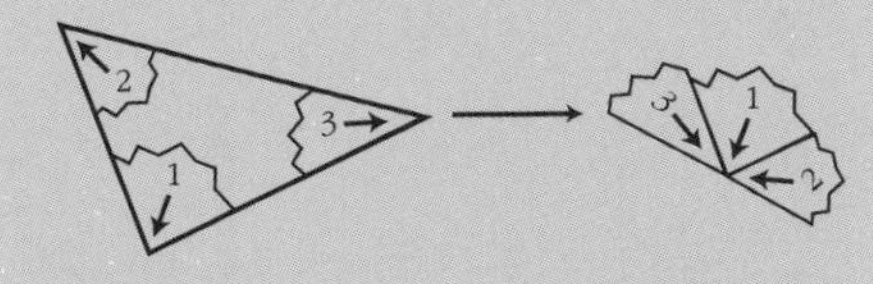

The three angles should fit together in such a way that they appear to form a total angle of 180°.

Ask students if this demonstration convinces them that the angles add up to 180° exactly. They should see that this demonstration, while more visual and perhaps more dramatic than the use of a protractor, is really no more of a proof about angle sums than measuring the angles is. It does not show the statement to be true for every triangle, and it is still only an approximation.

- *Quadrilaterals*

Note: The discussion of Question 2 can be delayed and made a part of tomorrow's discussion of tonight's homework. As part of that discussion, students will look at why the angle sum for quadrilaterals should be exactly twice that for triangles. You should *not* deal with that issue now unless students raise it on their own. If it does come up now, you can use tomorrow's notes for ideas on how to respond.

Let students share their conclusions about angle sums for quadrilaterals. They will probably see that the sum always appears to be approximately 360°.

Bring out that this observation, like the one for triangles, is only a conjecture (at least for now), since the measurements are only approximations. Also, have students discuss how their results on *Pattern Block Angles* fit this conjecture. Their results for the four quadrilateral blocks should all confirm the conjecture.

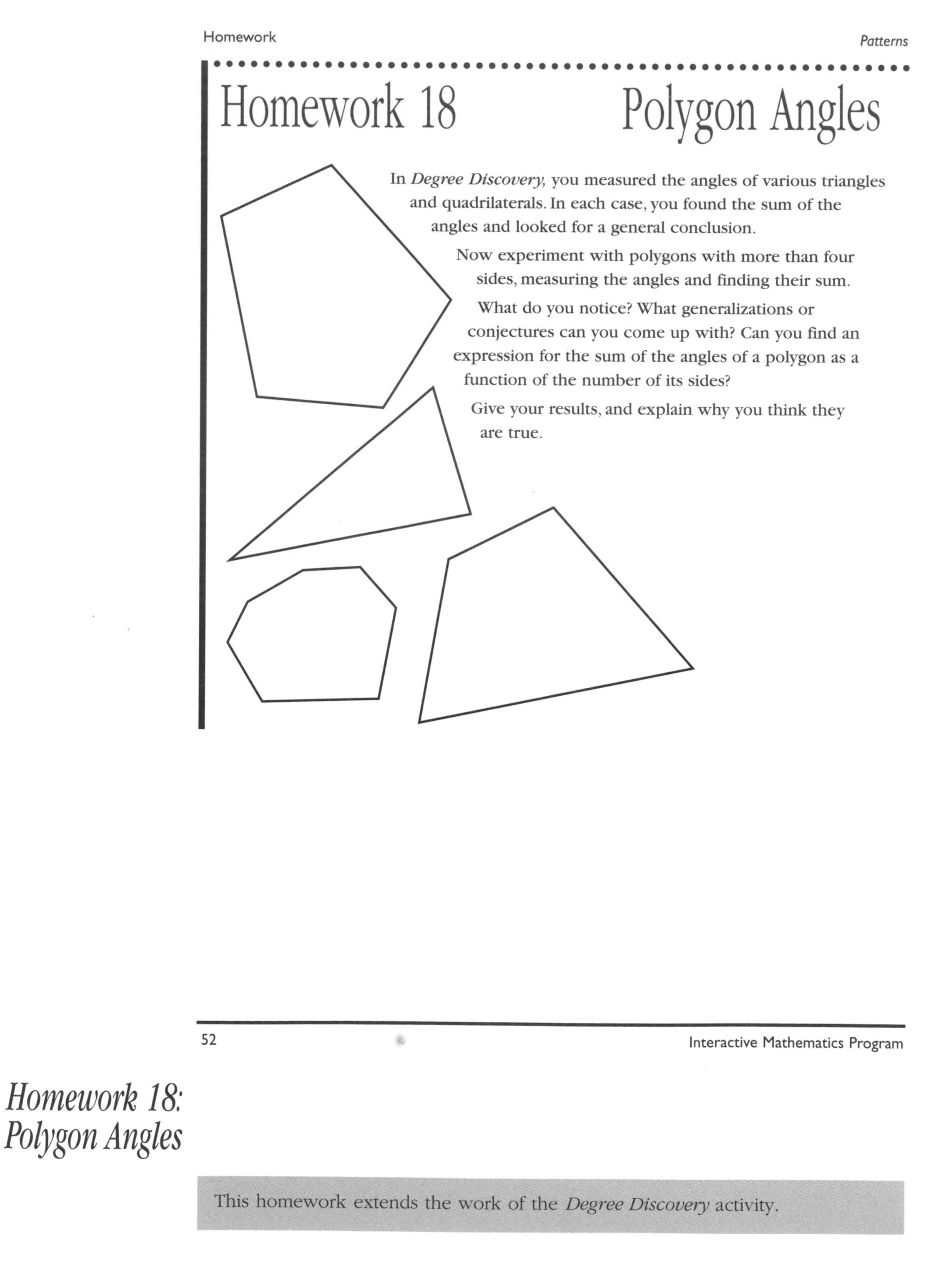

Homework 18 Polygon Angles

In *Degree Discovery,* you measured the angles of various triangles and quadrilaterals. In each case, you found the sum of the angles and looked for a general conclusion.

Now experiment with polygons with more than four sides, measuring the angles and finding their sum.

What do you notice? What generalizations or conjectures can you come up with? Can you find an expression for the sum of the angles of a polygon as a function of the number of its sides?

Give your results, and explain why you think they are true.

Homework 18: Polygon Angles

This homework extends the work of the *Degree Discovery* activity.

DAY 19 Angles of Polygons

Students develop a general formula for the sum of the angles of a polygon and look at an incorrect proof concerning angle sums.

Mathematical Topics

- Angle sums for polygons
- Proving the general angle sum formula for polygons from the assumption that the angle sum for triangles is 180°
- Finding a flaw in a proof and fixing the proof

Outline of the Day

In Class

1. Remind students to bring write-ups of *POW 3: Checkerboard Squares* to share in class tomorrow
2. Discuss *Homework 18: Polygon Angles*
   - Develop a general formula for angle sum for a polygon in terms of the number of sides
3. Discuss proving the angle sum formula for quadrilaterals based on the formula for triangles
4. *A Proof Gone Bad*
   - Students look at and fix an incorrect proof of the angle sum formula for quadrilaterals
5. Discuss *A Proof Gone Bad*
   - Have students identify the flaw
   - Revisit the earlier proof for quadrilaterals and generalize the reasoning to arbitrary polygons

At Home

Homework 19: An Angular Summary

Discuss With Your Colleagues

Proof Without Axioms?

In the traditional high school curriculum, proof has often been a formalized process with "statements" and "reasons," sometimes in a

special, two-column format. And it has usually been tied exclusively to Euclidean geometry, with its structure of axioms and postulates.

But mathematicians don't really think that way. When they read a proof of a statement, they mostly just want to gain insight into the question, "Why is it true?" They want to understand how the ideas work.

Several activities in this unit offer opportunities for students to write explanations for why something is true. *Homework 2: Who's Who?* and *Homework 12: That's Odd!* are examples that are unrelated to geometry. The discussion of the angle sum formula on Day 19 involves proof in geometry but without the axiomatic structure associated with Euclid. Several supplemental problems also involve proof.

Share student work on these problems with other teachers. Discuss what you consider to be "a real proof" and what you don't (see the subheading "What's a real proof?" on Day 13). Look at the paper-cutting activity on Day 18 and discuss why this is not a proof.

1. POW Sharing Tomorrow

Tell students to bring their write-ups of *POW 3: Checkerboard Squares* to class tomorrow. Students will share their write-ups with their group members and discuss what makes a good write-up. Tell them that it will be an excellent opportunity to "test" their POW write-up before turning it in.

Presentations of *POW 3: Checkerboard Squares* will take place on Day 21.

2. Discussion of *Homework 18: Polygon Angles*

You may want to begin by asking students to review what they saw yesterday about angle sums for triangles and quadrilaterals, so that the values of 180° and 360° are at least suggested as likely possibilities.

Then let different heart card students give you their conclusions about angle sums for polygons with more sides. Although their measurements will again be approximate, they will probably come up with conjectures that can be put into an In-Out table like the one below.

Number of sides	Angle sum
3	180°
4	360°
5	540°
6	720°
7	900°

Note: If students' measurements are not even close to these results, you probably need to take more time to talk about how to use a protractor.

- *Developing a generalization*

Take this table as far as students' homework results lead, and then ask whether anyone came up with a general formula expressing the angle sum as a function of the number of sides.

If you get a clear statement of the generalization, try to determine whether the class sees where the formula came from. If not, you can build up to the formula by asking students to guess what the angle sum would be for polygons with a specific number of sides not covered yet, based on the information in the table.

"What do you think is the sum of the angles in a ten-sided polygon?"

For example, if the table goes up to a seven-sided polygon, ask them to use the table to formulate a conjecture for ten-sided polygons. They should probably be able to extend the table by adding 180° three times to get additional rows, and you can put these rows into the table. By now, students will probably have recognized that all the *Out* values seem to be multiples of 180°.

"What should you multiply 180° by to get the sum of the angles of a 100-sided polygon?"

You can follow up with a large numerical case, such as a 100-sided polygon. At this point, the issue should be something like, "What should you multiply 180° by to get the sum of the angles of a 100-sided polygon?" Students should be able to confirm that the necessary factor seems to be found by subtracting 2 from the number of sides.

Add a row to the table to show this formula. The table might now look like the one below.

Number of sides	Angle sum
3	180°
4	360°
5	540°
6	720°
7	900°
8	1080°
9	1260°
10	1440°
100	17640°
n	$(n - 2)180°$

3. Proving the Angle Sum Formula

Remind students that their work so far only gives these results as *conjectures.* Tell them that these conjectures are actually correct and can be proved. Tell them, more specifically, that in a later Year 1 unit called *Shadows* they will see a proof of the conjecture for triangles; but meanwhile, they are going to see how they can prove a general formula for polygons based on the formula for triangles.

In other words, they are going to take the conjecture for triangles as an assumption for now. They will work from that assumption to understand angle sums for polygons with more sides, and then later in the year come back to the triangle conjecture.

• *From triangles to quadrilaterals*

"Why should the angle sum for quadrilaterals be exactly twice that for triangles?"

Ask if anyone can give a reason why the angle sum for quadrilaterals should be exactly twice that for triangles. You may want to have them discuss this in their groups. If absolutely necessary, you can suggest that they draw an arbitrary quadrilateral and think about how they can regard this as "twice" a triangle.

They should be able to see clearly that a diagonal will split a quadrilateral into two triangles. Without getting into a lot of detail, use that fact to conclude that the angle sum for the quadrilateral is the sum of the angle sums for its two triangles. Emphasize that this argument does not prove that the angle sum for a triangle is 180°, or even prove that every triangle has the same angle sum. It *does* prove that *if* every triangle has an angle sum of 180°, then every quadrilateral has an angle sum of 360°.

> *Note:* You will probably want to revisit this proof after discussing the next activity. See the heading "Another look at the one-diagonal proof."

4. *A Proof Gone Bad*

(see facing page)

At this point, have students look at the activity called *A Proof Gone Bad* and work in their groups to answer the questions it poses.

You may want to have some groups do write-ups on overhead transparencies.

5. Discussion of *A Proof Gone Bad*

"Where did Jerry's proof go wrong?"

Ask for volunteers to show where Jerry's proof went wrong. Some students may say that Jerry should have drawn only one diagonal. This criticism of the proof is likely to be based on the mistaken idea that the only correct proof is

A Proof Gone Bad

Jerry thought he had it all figured out. He was supposed to be writing a proof to show that the sum of the angles of a quadrilateral is 360°, based on the assumption that the sum for any triangle is 180°.

But when he looked over his work, it seemed to show that the sum for a quadrilateral is 720°.

Here's the proof he wrote.

Take any quadrilateral, such as the figure shown at the right (formed by the solid lines).

Then draw its diagonals (shown as dotted lines).

As you can see, this breaks the quadrilateral into four small triangles. We are assuming that the angles of each triangle add up to 180°, so the sum of the angles of the quadrilateral is $4 \cdot 180°$, which is 720°. Since this can be done with any quadrilateral, it must be true that the sum of the angles of any quadrilateral is 720°.

1. Explain what went wrong with Jerry's proof.
2. Write a correct proof based on Jerry's diagram.

the one discussed earlier, in which one diagonal is drawn. If this criticism comes up, bring out that there is nothing inherently wrong with drawing two diagonals, but that the diagram must then be used properly, which Jerry's argument does not do.

The real flaw in Jerry's proof is that the angles of his four triangles are not all parts of angles of the quadrilateral. If no one sees this, you might have students draw a diagram like Jerry's and measure the various angles—both the angles of the individual triangles and the angles of the quadrilateral. Ask what relationships exist between angles of the triangles and angles of the quadrilateral, and which angles of the triangles are not accounted for in these relationships.

The key is to see that the four angles formed by the intersection of the diagonals do not correspond to angles (or parts of angles) of the quadrilateral. Students should be able to explain that these four angles total 360°. From that, they can see that the sum of the angles of the quadrilateral is 360° less than the total sum of the angles of the four triangles.

So Jerry just needs to subtract 360° from his previous total of 720° to fix his proof.

- ***Optional: Another look at the one-diagonal proof***

You may want to use the discussion above to reexamine the proof of the angle sum for quadrilaterals discussed earlier. In that proof, a diagonal was used to divide the quadrilateral into two triangles. Students may have thought, "Since there are two triangles, the angle sum is twice that of one triangle." They probably did not stop to consider whether the angles of those two triangles really matched up to the angles of the quadrilateral.

Now that they have seen, through *A Proof Gone Bad,* that one needs to think about how the angles match up, they may be ready for a more careful look at their earlier work.

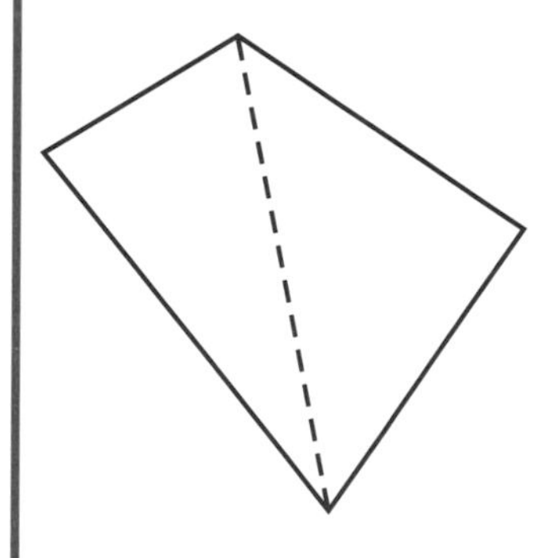

You can ask students to look at a diagram like the one at the left and explain exactly how the angles of the two triangles are related to the angles of the quadrilateral.

They should see that two of the angles of the quadrilateral are each angles of one of the triangles, while the other two angles of the quadrilateral are each composed of one angle from each triangle.

- ***The general polygon***

Finally, ask how the argument for quadrilaterals might be used to explain the formula for the general polygon. Here are two approaches that students might use.

- They may see (using more examples, if needed) that a polygon with n sides can be divided, using diagonals, into $n - 2$ triangles.
- They may see that a single diagonal can be used to divide an n-sided polygon into a triangle and an $(n - 1)$-sided polygon. This explains why each side added to the polygon increases the angle sum by 180°. (*Note:* This approach is another example of recursive reasoning—see discussion of *Homework 17: Diagonally Speaking*.)

Homework 19 An Angular Summary

Through your work on *Homework 18: Polygon Angles* and the discussion of that assignment, you have seen a formula that gives the sum of the angles of a polygon in terms of the number of sides it has.

1. Summarize what you know about the sum of the angles of a polygon, and explain the reasoning behind any formulas you include.
2. A **regular polygon** is a polygon that has all of its angles equal and all of its sides equal.
   a. Use the formula about angle sums to find the size of each of the angles for the following regular polygons. Explain your reasoning.
      i. A regular pentagon (five sides)
      ii. A regular octagon (eight sides)
   b. Draw each of the polygons in Question 2a, using a protractor to get the angles to be the right size. (You can decide on the lengths for the sides in each case. The sides of your pentagon do not need to have the same length as the sides of your octagon.)

Homework 19: An Angular Summary

This assignment will require students to synthesize their work of the past few days.

Putting It Together

This page in the student book introduces Days 20 through 24.

In the last few days of *Patterns,* you'll be applying some of the ideas you've learned to problems that involve both numbers and geometry. These problems will give you a chance to see more ways to use In-Out tables, and you'll also learn how to make your graphing calculator act like an In-Out machine.

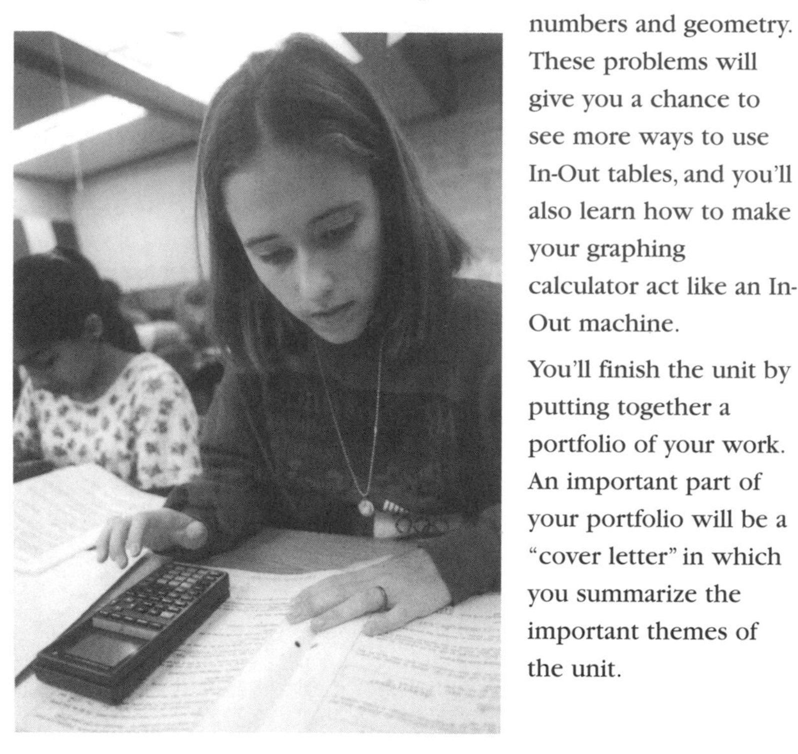

Laura Harr writes a program to make her graphing calculator act like an In-Out machine.

You'll finish the unit by putting together a portfolio of your work. An important part of your portfolio will be a "cover letter" in which you summarize the important themes of the unit.

DAY 20 POW Sharing

Students share their POWs and think about what makes a good POW write-up.

Mathematical Topics

- Summarizing principles about angle sums for polygons
- Developing skill in writing about mathematics

Outline of the Day

In Class

1. Discuss *Homework 19: An Angular Summary*
2. Have students share write-ups of *POW 3: Checkerboard Squares*
3. Select presenters for tomorrow's discussion of *POW 3: Checkerboard Squares*

At Home

Homework 20: Squares and Scoops

1. Discussion of *Homework 19: An Angular Summary*

You may want to have one or two volunteers read or present their work on Question 1, and let the class add to or correct the material presented.

Be sure to get some explanations for the angle sum formula. These might refer, for example, to the idea of subdividing a polygon into triangles or to the numerical pattern found in *Homework 18: Polygon Angles*.

You can use this as another occasion to bring out that the basic fact about angle sums for triangles is still just an experimental observation.

On Question 2, you can ask spade card students to explain their work on part a, and then ask what difficulties students had in drawing the polygons. This may lead to some review of the use of protractors.

2. POW Sharing

Ask students to take out their write-ups for *POW 3: Checkerboard Squares*. Since this is their third POW, they should have formed some idea of what is expected of them, but seeing each other's work will nonetheless probably be of great value.

You can have students pass their POW write-up to the group member to their left. Every two minutes or so they should rotate papers.

As they read, have students focus on what makes a good paper, what makes an adequate paper, and what makes a poor paper. They will spend time today discussing those questions.

It is probably inevitable that the problem itself will be discussed in the course of talking about the quality of the write-ups, but that is not the intended focus for today. So don't push for an analysis of the problem; leave that for tomorrow's POW discussion.

- *Students without POWs*

There will no doubt be some students who will come to class without their POW write-up, either because they forgot it or because they have not done it yet. Although these students do not have a write-up to share, have them read write-ups also. Some students are bound to finish reading before others and they can pass their write-ups to those who did not bring theirs.

It may seem unfair to those who worked hard to come up with an answer that others will get to see their paper and not have to do the work themselves. This would be a good time to talk more about the IMP philosophy. One point to make is that working through the problem is the most important part of a POW and anyone who simply takes another's answer is going to get much less out of the problem.

An equally important point to make is that you want an atmosphere of cooperation and collaboration in your classroom. This means you not only *want* students to share whenever possible, you *expect* them to share whenever possible.

- *Focused free-writing on POW write-ups*

After the sharing of POW write-ups is completed, ask students to do focused free-writing on the topic "What makes a good POW write-up."

"What do you consider important in a POW write-up? Why?"

After they have written for about five minutes, let students share their ideas. They can read aloud from their written work or simply say about what they thought about.

- *POWs to be revised*

At the end of this discussion, students should be sure to get their write-ups back. They can continue to work on them for tomorrow, incorporating what they learned today.

3. POW Presentation Preparation

Choose three students to make POW presentations, and give them overhead pens and transparencies to take home to use in their preparations. You may want to choose the presenters who seem to have done a good job, based on what you saw and heard in class today. (They should nevertheless be students who have not done POW presentations yet.)

Homework 20: Squares and Scoops

(see next page)

In each of the two homework problems, students are likely to see the *Out* in terms of the previous *Out,* rather than directly in terms of the *In.* They may also see an analogy between summation notation and factorials.

Amanda Burley, Christina Mardirosian, and Laura Galvan study angle sums in their pattern block design (Day 16).

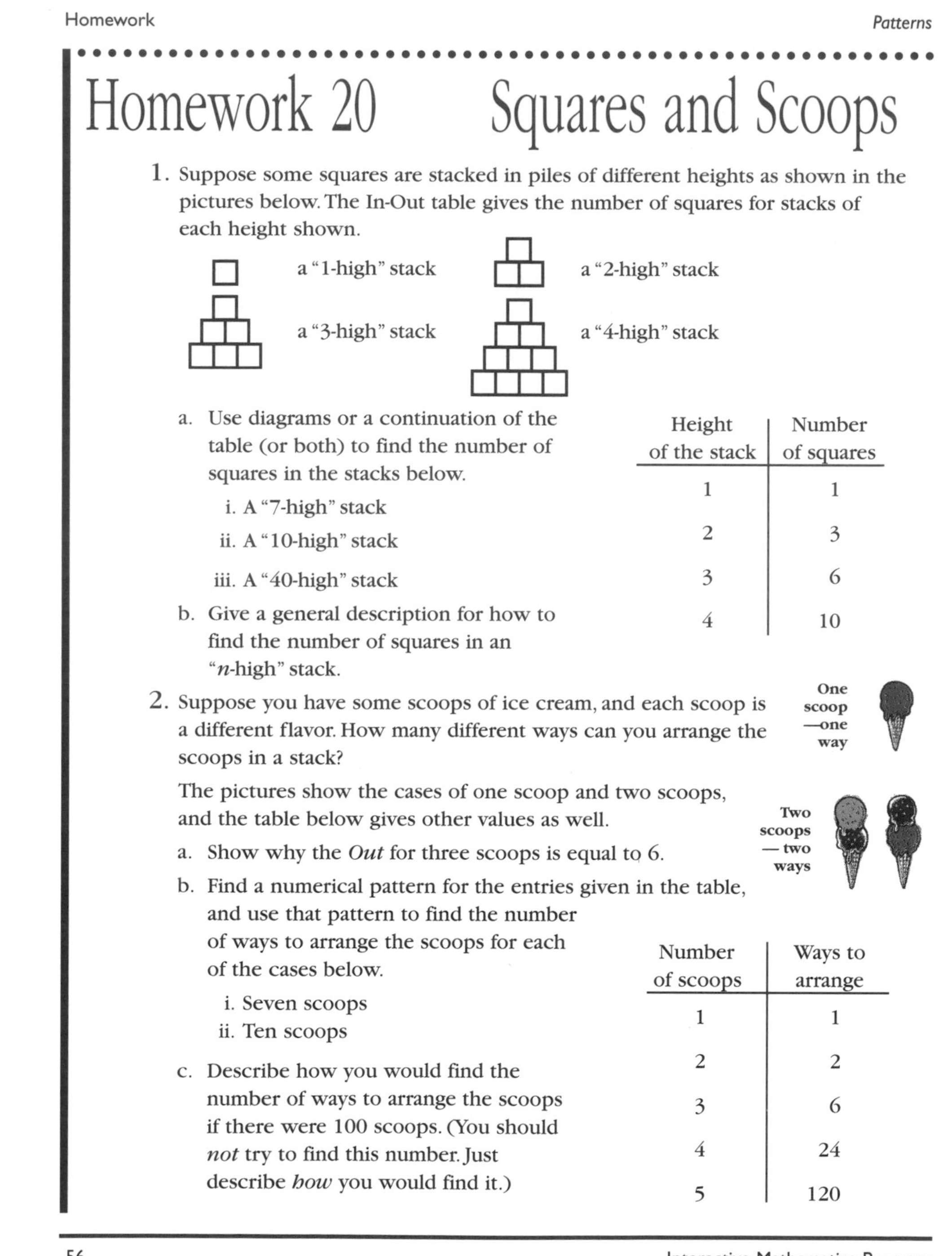

Homework 20 Squares and Scoops

1. Suppose some squares are stacked in piles of different heights as shown in the pictures below. The In-Out table gives the number of squares for stacks of each height shown.

a "1-high" stack a "2-high" stack

a "3-high" stack a "4-high" stack

a. Use diagrams or a continuation of the table (or both) to find the number of squares in the stacks below.

i. A "7-high" stack

ii. A "10-high" stack

iii. A "40-high" stack

b. Give a general description for how to find the number of squares in an "*n*-high" stack.

Height of the stack	Number of squares
1	1
2	3
3	6
4	10

2. Suppose you have some scoops of ice cream, and each scoop is a different flavor. How many different ways can you arrange the scoops in a stack?

One scoop—one way

The pictures show the cases of one scoop and two scoops, and the table below gives other values as well.

Two scoops—two ways

a. Show why the *Out* for three scoops is equal to 6.

b. Find a numerical pattern for the entries given in the table, and use that pattern to find the number of ways to arrange the scoops for each of the cases below.

i. Seven scoops

ii. Ten scoops

c. Describe how you would find the number of ways to arrange the scoops if there were 100 scoops. (You should *not* try to find this number. Just describe *how* you would find it.)

Number of scoops	Ways to arrange
1	1
2	2
3	6
4	24
5	120

DAY 21

POW 3 Presentations

Students do POW presentations and also discuss the two patterns from the homework.

Mathematical Topics

- Analyzing and explaining a geometric problem in terms of an arithmetic pattern
- Expressing problem situations by using In-Out tables and by finding rules for the tables
- Using the concepts of "summation" and "factorial" in a problem context

Outline of the Day

In Class

1. Presentations of *POW 3: Checkerboard Squares*
   - Focus on clear explanations for the result and for generalizations
2. Discuss *Homework 20: Squares and Scoops*

At Home

Homework 21: The Garden Border

Note: Tomorrow students will be developing and then entering a program in their calculators to simulate an In-Out machine. The conceptual basis of the program will be dealt with in tomorrow's discussion.

However, you may want to work with a small group of students before then (perhaps outside the class) so that they are familiar with what keys need to be pressed to enter a given instruction. They will then be able to serve as facilitators and to assist the class in entering the program.

In addition (or instead), you may wish to prepare an overhead transparency for tomorrow's class giving key-by-key instructions for entering the program. Or you may prefer to write up the instructions together with the students during the class.

1. Presentations of *POW 3: Checkerboard Squares*

Note: Discussion of last night's homework is scheduled to follow the POW presentations.

Have the assigned students give their presentations on *POW 3: Checkerboard Squares*. In the discussion that grows out of the reports, focus on the patterns that students have discovered. Bring out that finding patterns in mathematics helps us in analyzing situations.

For an 8×8 checkerboard, students will probably have seen that the number of squares of a given size grows as the size decreases.

- There is one 8×8 square.
- There are four 7×7 squares.
- There are nine 6×6 squares.
- There are sixteen 5×5 squares, and so forth.

Possible questions: "Why is the number of squares of each size itself a square number? Why is it the particular square that it is?"

Have students justify this analysis, rather than simply state it. That is, ask students to explain why the number of squares of a given size is itself the square of a number, and why it is the particular square that it is.

For example, students might use a process such as sliding a square of a given size down and across the checkerboard while counting how many such squares there are. Thus, the sequence of pictures below shows the nine 6×6 squares and can also be used to explain why the number of squares is 3^2.

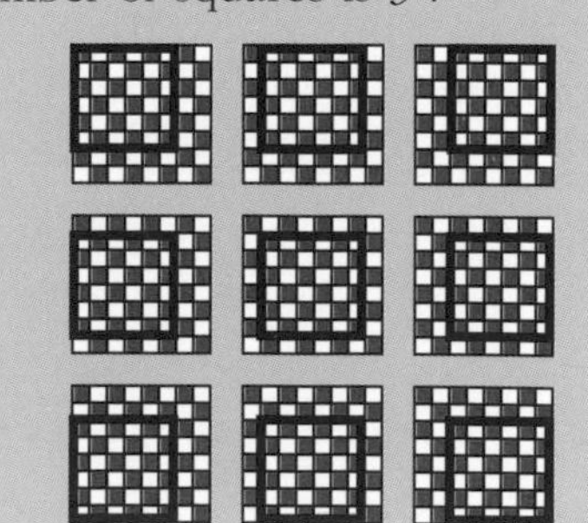

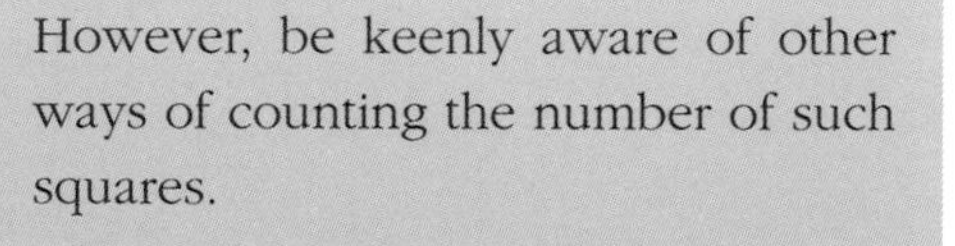

However, be keenly aware of other ways of counting the number of such squares.

Note: This problem provides an opportunity for a nice digression about the geometric and arithmetic meanings of the word "square." Use your judgment whether to pursue this.

- *Optional: Using summation notation*

This problem provides an opportunity to put the Σ notation to good use. (Another occurs in today's discussion of last night's homework.)

You can ask students how to express the total number of squares using summation notation. They should be able to come up with something like

$$\sum_{t=1}^{8} t^2$$

More generally, the number of squares in an $n \times n$ checkerboard is

$$\sum_{t=1}^{n} t^2$$

2. Discussion of *Homework 20: Squares and Scoops*

You may want to give students time to share processes and solution on this assignment with their group members. Then bring the whole class together to compare ideas.

- *Question 1*

In Question 1, students may use either a pattern in the table or the pictures themselves to find the number of squares for the heights requested.

For example, they may look at the table and see that the *Out* entries are increasing by 2, then by 3, and then by 4. They should be able to continue this pattern to find the number of squares in a 7-high stack. That is, they may start with the value of ten squares for a 4-high stack, and then successively add 5, 6, and 7 to get the value for a 7-high stack.

If you used the term *recursive function* in discussing *Homework 17: Diagonally Speaking,* you may want to use that term again to describe this analysis of the table.

Probably some students will prefer to work with the pictures, saying, for example, that a 7-high stack has a row with seven squares, a row with six squares, and so on; therefore the total number of squares is

$$7 + 6 + 5 + 4 + 3 + 2 + 1$$

In either case, they should be able to see that the number of squares in an n-high stack can be found by adding the numbers from 1 to n.

You may want to mention that the *Outs* in this problem are known as **triangular numbers** because of the triangular shape of the stacks.

You can ask students how to express the result using summation notation. They should be able to write it as something like

$$\sum_{r=1}^{n} r$$

(Students who expressed the sum as going from 7 down to 1 may need a hint.)

Note: The supplemental problem *From One to N* asks students to develop an expression for finding this sum without doing repeated addition.

- *Question 2*

The main purpose of Question 2 is to get students to articulate and use the pattern of the *Out* values. They should see that each *Out* can be found by multiplying the *In* by the previous *Out*. For example, the number of ways to arrange five scoops is 5 times 24. (You can identify this as another example of a recursive function.)

They should be able to use this pattern to find the specific values asked for in Question 2b.

As with Question 1, students may also see that each output can be obtained "from scratch" as well as from the previous value. For example, they may see that, just as 120 is $5 \cdot 24$, so also 24 is $4 \cdot 6$, and so on, and ultimately 120 is obtained as $5 \cdot 4 \cdot 3 \cdot 2 \cdot 1$. (Students may choose to omit the factor of 1.)

The discussion of Question 2c may help to bring this out. Even if students begin with the value for ten scoops, they will probably say something like, "Multiply this by 11, then by 12, then by 13, and so on, all the way up to 100."

Students may recognize the nth output as ***n* factorial** (written $n!$). (The factorial concept was mentioned in *POW 2: 1-2-3-4 Puzzle.*) Students may also describe the rule by saying "Multiply the *In* by all the *Ins* before it."

Although Question 2a asks students to explain the *Out* value for three scoops, the discussion should focus on the numerical pattern of the *Out* values and not on an analysis based on permutations.

These types of counting problems, as well as more complex problems of a similar nature, are a major focus of the Year 3 unit *Pennant Fever.* In fact, the distinction between scoops of ice cream stacked on a cone and scoops placed in a bowl plays an important role in that unit.

- *Optional: The analogy between the patterns*

You may want to ask students if they see any similarity between the two stacking problems. They may recognize that Question 1 involves addition of the integers from 1 to n and Question 2 involves their product.

For your information: There is standard notation for products similar to that for sums. It uses the capital Greek letter pi (Π) in place of sigma.

For example,

$$\prod_{t=3}^{7} t$$

means $3 \cdot 4 \cdot 5 \cdot 6 \cdot 7$.

- ***Some further ideas***

The patterns in these problems would be much harder to find if the entries were not arranged sequentially. You can remind students that while this is a good principle for analyzing information, the entries of an In-Out table do not, in general, have to be arranged in any particular order.

"Is 1.5 an appropriate input for either of these tables?"

You can also ask the class about the appropriateness of fractional inputs for these two In-Out tables. Inputs such as 1.5 or 6.7 do not make sense for either problem.

"What do you call the set of possible inputs for an In-Out table?"

You can ask students if they remember a term that refers to the set of inputs that are permitted or that make sense for a particular In-Out table. Remind them of the term *domain* if needed.

"What other examples have you seen where only certain inputs were allowed?"

Lastly, ask students if they can think of other tables where only certain kinds of inputs are allowed, that is, where not everything is in the domain.

Homework 21: The Garden Border

(see next page)

This homework offers students another opportunity to generalize and a chance to see many different ways to approach the same problem.

This assignment is followed up in tomorrow night's *Homework 22: Border Varieties.*

If you have time to introduce the assignment, emphasize to students that they are not to count the tiles one by one, but are to come up with methods for finding the number of tiles without counting them individually. They should try to create a diagram that explains each method.

Homework 21 The Garden Border

Leslie was planning an ornamental garden.

She wanted the garden to be square, 10 feet on each side, and she wanted part of this area to be used for a border of tiles. The tiles she wanted were each 1 foot by 1 foot square.

Leslie had to figure out how many tiles she needed.

Your challenge is to figure out how many tiles Leslie needed without counting the tiles individually. Write down as many ways as you can for doing this, giving the specific arithmetic involved in detail.

For each method that you find, draw a diagram that indicates how that method works.

DAY 22

Calculator Programming

Students program their graphing calculators to act like In-Out machines.

Mathematical Topics

- Seeing different ways to solve a problem
- Writing a plan for programming a graphing calculator to behave like an In-Out machine
- Using variables in programming
- Entering a calculator program

Outline of the Day

In Class

1. Discuss *Homework 21: The Garden Border*
2. Write a program to make a graphing calculator act like an In-Out machine
   - Introduce the use of variables
   - Develop the outline by programming a human calculator
   - Turn the outline into a formal program
   - Students enter and use the program
   - Post the program for use tomorrow

At Home

Homework 22: Border Varieties

Special Materials Needed

- Overhead projector for calculator display (if available)

Discuss With Your Colleagues

Calculators and Programming

What do students learn from writing the programs used on Days 22 and 23? How do you help students distinguish between the big ideas involved, such as the use of variables, and the petty mechanics of programming, such as whether you need to use a multiplication sign or knowing which key will accomplish a given task?

This type of activity can be particularly intimidating when you, yourself, are not yet at home with the new technology of graphing calculators. Share your anxieties with each other and discuss how to make meaningful mathematical learning out of programming.

1. Discussion of *Homework 21: The Garden Border*

You can ask the club card members of various group to report on one of the methods used to calculate the number of tiles in the border. The reporting student should give the details of the arithmetic as well as a diagram.

For example, one method is to use the fact that there are ten tiles along each edge, then subtract four to account for the fact that each corner tile is on two edges. For this method, the arithmetic might look like "$4 \cdot 10 - 4$."

There are various diagrams that might be used to represent this method. The diagram below shows the four 10's along the edges and then the four corner tiles that have been counted twice. (A more schematic diagram appears in tonight's homework.)

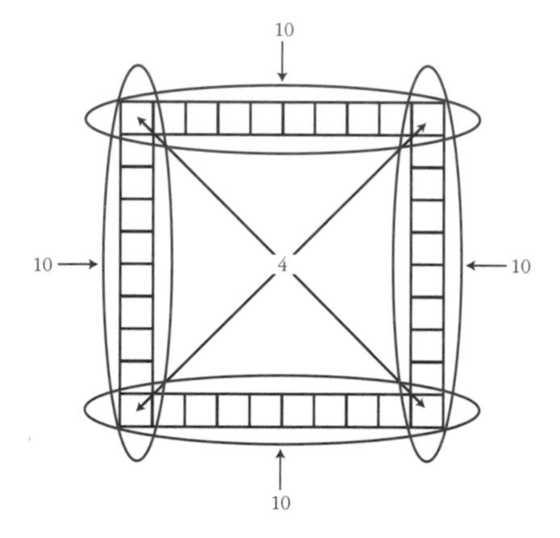

Once the club card students have reported, ask for any additional ways not yet mentioned. Collect as many approaches as students can come up with.

Take a few minutes to talk about how some of the strategies collected might be applied to a 5×5 square. For example, applying the method described above to a 5×5 square would show that such a square uses $4 \cdot 5 - 4 = 16$ tiles.

2. Programming In-Out Machines on the Calculator

The remainder of the period is devoted to a discussion of how to program the graphing calculators to act like In-Out machines.

Tell students that they will be learning how to create an In-Out machine program on the calculators, and that after they have learned the necessary programming, they will make up problems to challenge each other (in tomorrow's activity, *Stump Your Friend*).

Keep in mind that this is the first time students are asked to use the graphing calculator in a way that exceeds the capabilities of an ordinary or scientific calculator (except perhaps for their work on *Calculator Exploration* on Day 2).

- ## *Programs and the use of variables*

Take some time to introduce the general idea of writing a program and using variables in programming. Though some students may be familiar with these matters, others will not be, and it's best to start from the beginning. (*Note:* This introduction is written as if you are to present all the information, but you may be able to draw some of the ideas from students and then supplement and clarify as needed.)

Tell students that for this programming activity, they should picture the calculator as a machine that can to do arithmetic and keep track of various numbers by naming them. Tell them that they will learn later about other specific capabilities of their particular calculators, but they don't need to know anything else about them for now.

"What is a program?"

Here are some key points to bring out about what a program is and does.

- It tells the calculator what arithmetic to do and when to do it.
- It tells the calculator how to keep track of the numbers involved.
- It is written using a very precise language, which may vary from machine to machine.

Concerning variables, you can tell students to imagine that the calculator has a collection of storage bins for keeping track of numbers. In order for the calculator to retrieve a number from one of these bins, the bin needs to have a label on it; therefore the program will have to tell the calculator how to label these bins as it uses them. Once a bin is labeled and has a number in it, students will be able to tell the calculator to "get" the number from that bin, and they also will be able to replace the number with another.

- ## *Programming a human calculator*

Before getting into the technical details of programming—that is, which keys to push to accomplish a given task—have students act out the process by having one student "be the calculator." The class will create a set of instructions for the volunteer who plays the role of the calculator.

You might begin by having that student make several squares (unlabeled) to represent the calculator's storage bins.

"What's a simple rule we might use as an example?"

Decide on a simple rule to use for the In-Out machine to be programmed. For this discussion, we will use the rule "Multiply the *In* by 4 and then subtract 3 from that product." (In symbols: $Out = 4 \cdot In - 3$.)

"How can we get the human calculator to behave like this In-Out machine?"

Now lead a discussion of how to get the human calculator to act in a way that resembles this In-Out machine. This will probably be somewhat loose in structure, since students may not know what they can and cannot do. Here are some key points to bring out.

- The calculator must be given the input. It therefore must be told, as part of the program, that it will get an input.
- The calculator must be told to store this input in one of its storage bins so that it can do arithmetic with it. This means giving that storage bin a label, usually a letter. In most calculators, this label is assigned in the same instruction that tells the calculator that it is supposed to get an input.
- The calculator must to be told what arithmetic to do with the input. In giving this instruction, the input should be referred to by the label on its storage bin.
- The calculator must do something with the result of its arithmetic calculation. This may be simply to display the result on its screen. Some machines first require the calculator to store the result in a storage bin.

Out of this discussion, develop a generic program for the human calculator. Keep it simple. Your outline might look something like this.

- Get a number and put it in a bin labeled N.
- Take the number in the bin labeled N and multiply it by 4, putting the result in a bin labeled P.
- Take the number in the bin labeled P and subtract 3 from it, putting the result in a bin labeled D.
- Take the number in the bin labeled D and say it out loud.

Tell students that some of these steps might be combined for some machines. Emphasize that the order of the steps is very important, just as order of operations is important in arithmetic.

Once the outline has been developed, or perhaps as trial programs have been worked out, test the program with the human calculator volunteer to see how well it works, and refine it as needed.

- *Entering the program in a calculator*

Have everyone take out a calculator for the task of turning this outline into a calculator program and entering it. As always, each student should have his or her own calculator to use, since it is important that each student gets to experience searching for the appropriate key, making mistakes, and so forth. At the same time, encourage students to work with each other, perhaps each with a partner.

> *Logistical suggestion:* If more than one class is sharing a set of calculators, you may want to use a different program name or program slot for each class.

There are several pedagogical styles that you might consider for the task of getting students to enter the program in their calculators. Your choice will probably depend both on your own personality and on the personality of your class. Of course, you may want to blend these methods.

Whichever method you use, you might find an overhead projector display of the calculator to be useful.

The "track shoes" approach. Put the written form of the program on an overhead transparency (perhaps prepared ahead of time) or prepare a handout to distribute to students. You may want to provide key-by-key instructions as well as the written program.

Then let students work on the program-entry process while you race from group to group, giving additional support as needed.

The "baby steps" approach. Again, make the written form of the program available, but keep the class working together as a whole. Use an overhead display of the calculator so that students can see which keys they should press and what should happen as they press them. Urge them not to jump ahead, pointing out that you won't be able to handle their questions out of sequence.

Go one small step at a time so that students can keep up in spite of the mistakes they make. With each instruction you give them and each key they press, connect what they are doing with the "human calculator" activity that just occurred.

The "feet on the desk" approach. You don't literally put your feet up, but in this approach you rely more on the students to help each other. They build on instructions from an overhead transparency or a handout and perhaps use calculator manuals to figure out the details of program entry.

Keep in mind that students are doing two things at once.

- They are learning which keys to press so that the program they enter will be correct.
- They are trying to understand the program itself.

Once the program has been entered, go over the mechanics of running the program. As with the process of entering the program, an overhead projector display of the calculator is helpful.

Finally, review the overall program so that students can see where and how they can make changes to create different In-Out machines. Review both the mathematical changes as well as the mechanics of editing a program.

Post the written form of the program. If you created key-by-key instructions for entering the program, post those also.

If the calculators you are using have a shortcut for rerunning a program just after it has been run, be sure students know that shortcut as well.

Homework 22 Border Varieties

Leslie decided it would be nice to have a general formula for her border problem, giving the number of tiles needed as a function of the size of the garden.

She imagined a square garden which was s feet on each side, and continued to work with square tiles that were 1 foot on each side.

She asked for some help from students who had worked on the border problem for the 10-by-10 square. Since they had solved it in different ways, they also came up with different formulas for the general problem.

For example, one student had counted ten tiles along each edge, and then subtracted 4 because the corner tiles had each been counted twice. In other words, this student's arithmetic looked like that shown at the right.

$$\begin{array}{r} 10 \\ \times 4 \\ \hline 40 \\ -4 \\ \hline 36 \end{array}$$

The student used the diagram at the right to explain this arithmetic and came up with the formula $4s - 4$ for the general border problem.

Continued on next page

Homework 22: Border Varieties

This homework asks students to generalize various methods for solving the border problem.

1. Shown below is the arithmetic used by five other students in the 10-by-10 case, along with a diagram that each student used to explain the arithmetic.

   For each of these methods, find a general formula that fits that student's way of thinking about the problem. Your formula should use *s* to represent the length of one side of the garden. Make your formula match the arithmetic as closely as possible.

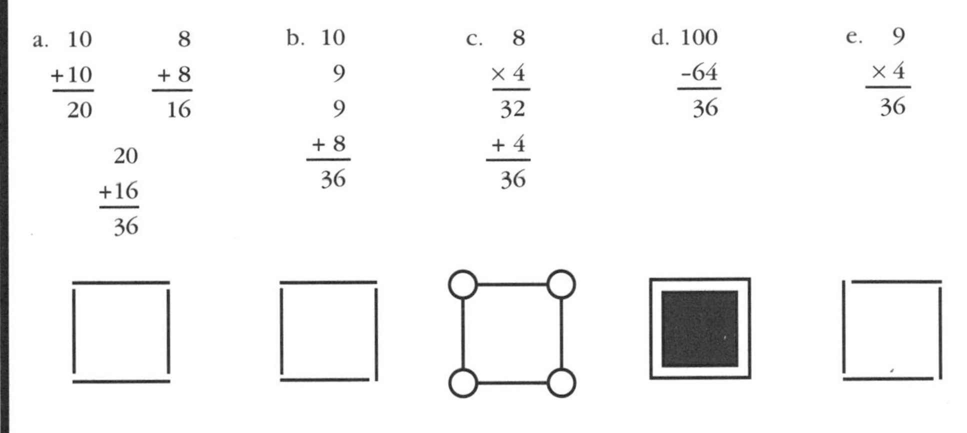

2. Give the arithmetic, a diagram, and a general formula for another method of solving the border problem.

DAY 23 Stump Your Friend

Students use graphing calculators to investigate rules for In-Out machines.

Mathematical Topics

- Finding different algebraic expressions to generalize the same problem
- Programming a graphing calculator to behave like an In-Out machine

Outline of the Day

In Class

1. Tell students to bring all their work from the unit to class tomorrow for assembling their portfolio
2. Discuss *Homework 22: Border Varieties*
3. *Stump Your Friend*
   - Students write calculator programs to represent different In-Out machines
   - Students try to find rules for each other's functions
   - No whole-class discussion of this activity is needed

At Home

Homework 23: Cutting Through the Layers

1. Portfolio Preparation

Tomorrow, students will be assembling a portfolio of their work from the *Patterns* unit. In preparation for this, tell students that they need to bring all of their work from this unit to class tomorrow.

2. Discussion of *Homework 22: Border Varieties*

Ask various students to share their answers to *Homework 22: Border Varieties*. They will probably want to use the diagrams that accompany the problem to explain how they got their answer. The pictures should make the generalizations more understandable to students who were unable to do the homework correctly.

Another technique to help clarify the generalizations is to do another specific case, such as $s = 100$. For example, on Question 1a, the picture should suggest that the border for a 100×100 garden would have 100 tiles along the top and 100 along the bottom, leaving 98 for each of the other two sides. Getting students to express this as $2 \cdot 100 + 2(100 - 2)$ should help you elicit the expression $2s + 2(s - 2)$. [Students might also express the method of Question 1a using the formula $s + s + (s - 2) + (s - 2)$.]

This might be a good homework to collect for general assessment as well as for grading. It should indicate how comfortable students are using variables to express generalizations.

3. Stump Your Friend

(see facing page)

In this activity, students will program different In-Out rules, or functions, into their calculators and pass the calculators to other students for them to figure out the rules.

The goal of this activity is to provide the students with more experience working with In-Out machines and with programming their calculators. It is not necessary for the entire class to discuss this activity.

- *Level of complexity*

You may want to give students guidance about the level of complexity of the rules they use. In some classes, it is best to insist that students start with very simple rules (for example, rules of the form $x + a$, ax, $a - x$, or $x \div a$, for some number a).

As you circulate among students and see how the activity is going, you may decide to suggest that they move to more complex functions, perhaps still restricting them somewhat. For example, you might suggest that they continue to use rules involving just the four fundamental arithmetic operations, but that they now use up to two operations in a given rule [this would then include rules such as $3x - 4$ or $(x + 5) \div 2$].

The goal is to make the process of figuring out the rules challenging but not overwhelming. The topic of In-Out machines needs to be viewed by the students as an area where it is okay to guess. Students will be working with In-Out tables, in one form or another, throughout the IMP curriculum, and they do not need to master techniques for finding rules at this time. Students should gradually gain experience with this over time and become comfortable exploring possibilities.

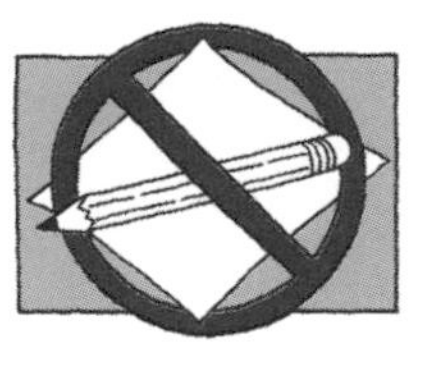

Stump Your Friend

The first part of your work in this activity is to write a program for the calculator to make it act like an In-Out machine.

After you have written your program (and tested it to be sure it works properly), trade calculators with someone else. Then each of you should attempt to find the rule that the other person programmed.

That is, each of you will run the other's program, making an In-Out table and looking for the rule. (You are on your honor not to look at the program itself—that's cheating.)

When you and the person you traded with think you have found each other's rules, check with each other to see if you are right.

Then get you calculator back and trade with someone else. Continue as long as time allows.

Note: It's possible that the same rule can be written in different ways. If the rule you find is different from the rule the other person used to write the calculator program, check more examples to see if your rule always gives the same *Out* values as the program. If it does, work together to see if you can figure out why the two "different" rules are really the same.

- *Equivalent rules*

The note at the end of the activity *Stump Your Friend* is intended as a very informal preview of the concept of equivalent expressions, which will be discussed in the Year 2 unit *Solve It!*

For example, a student may write a program that says to double the *In* and then add 6. Another student may come up with the rule "Add three to the *In* and then double." You should encourage the two students to talk about whether this is a correct description of the In-Out machine or not, and why, but keep this at an informal level.

Homework 23: Cutting Through the Layers

(see facing page)

The final homework of the unit provides yet another opportunity for students to use variables to state a generalization. In this assignment, students deal with a problem involving two inputs and are asked to explain their general formula in terms of the problem situation.

Matt Camacho and Mike Duva prepare wall charts for their oral presentations.

Homework 23 Cutting Through the Layers

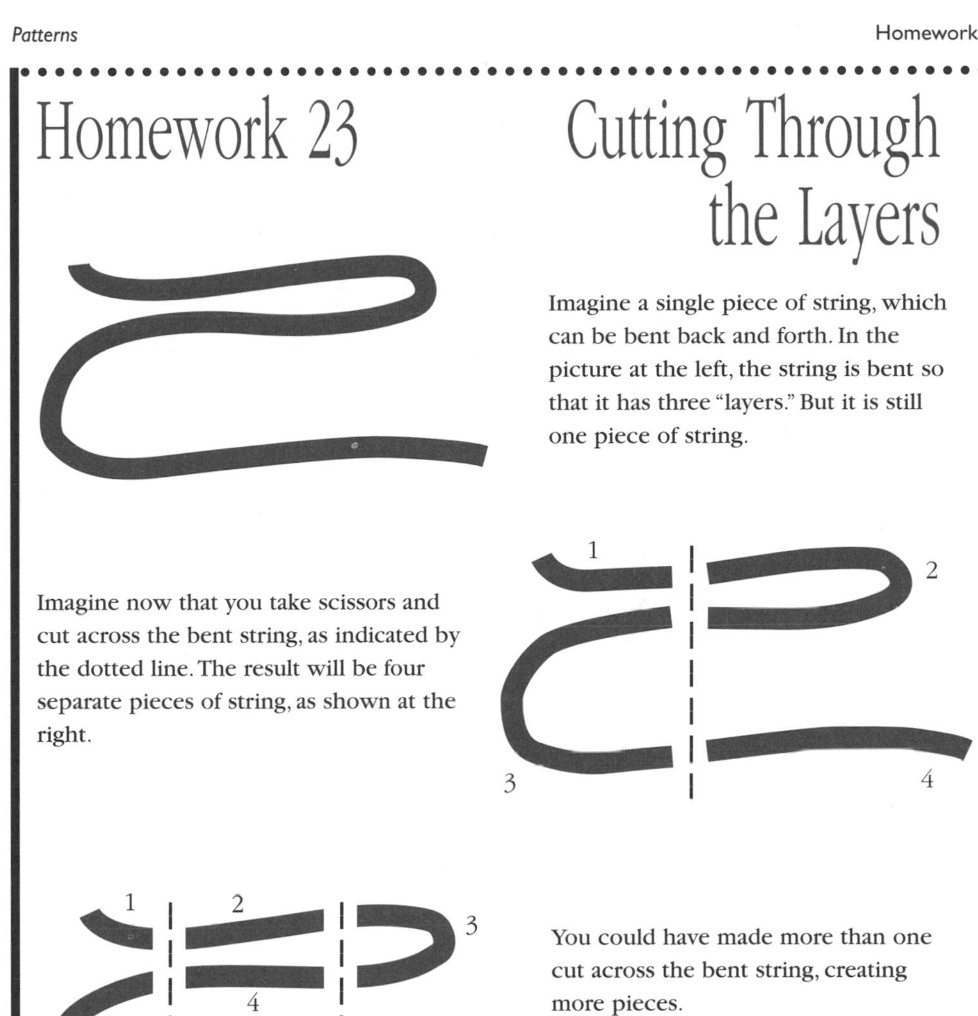

Imagine a single piece of string, which can be bent back and forth. In the picture at the left, the string is bent so that it has three "layers." But it is still one piece of string.

Imagine now that you take scissors and cut across the bent string, as indicated by the dotted line. The result will be four separate pieces of string, as shown at the right.

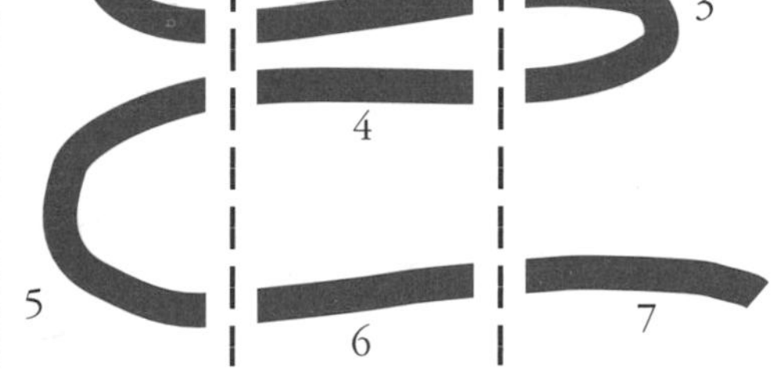

You could have made more than one cut across the bent string, creating more pieces.

In the picture at the left, two cuts have been made, creating a total of seven pieces.

Continued on next page

You could also start with more layers in the bent string.

In the picture at the right, there are four layers and three cuts. That creates a total of 13 pieces.

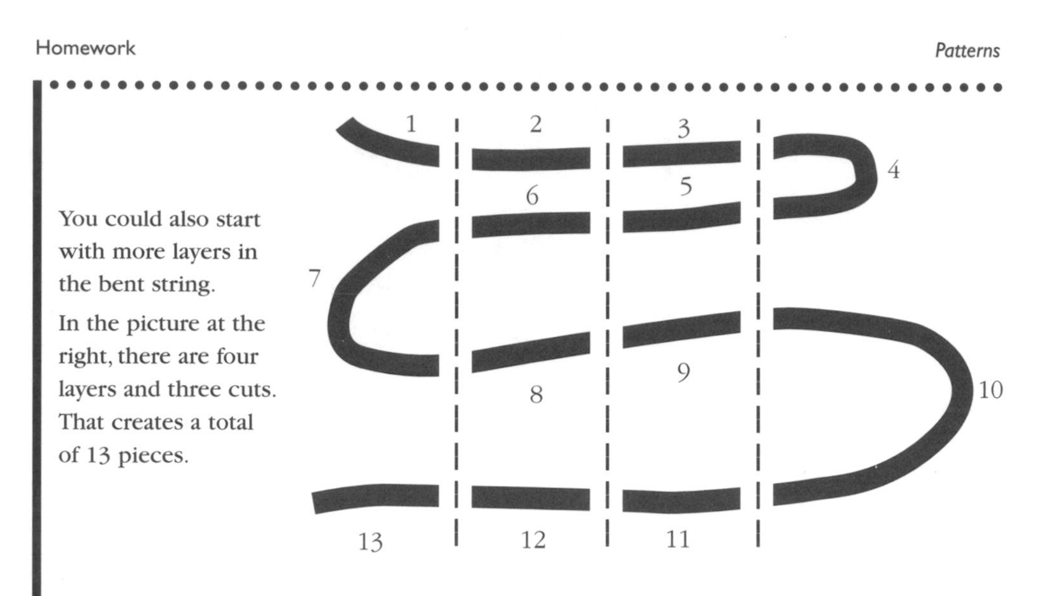

All of this information about layers, cuts, and pieces of string has been organized into the In-Out table below. Since the number of pieces depends on both the numbers of layers and the number of cuts, there are two inputs, while the number of pieces is the output.

Inputs		Output
Number of layers	Number of cuts	Number of pieces
3	0	1
3	1	4
3	2	7
4	3	13

1. Make your own pictures of string with different numbers of layers and different numbers of cuts. Count the pieces and add that information to the In-Out table.

2. Suppose the number of layers is L and the number of cuts is C. Find a rule or formula expressing the number of pieces as a function of both L and C. In other words, tell what to do with L and C to find out how many pieces there will be.

Portfolios

Students compile their portfolios for the unit.

Mathematical Topics

- Developing an In-Out table involving two inputs
- Finding an algebraic expression for a two-input In-Out table
- Reviewing the unit and preparing portfolios

Outline of the Day

In Class

1. Remind students that unit assessments will take place tomorrow and tomorrow night
2. Discuss *Homework 23: Cutting Through the Layers*
3. *"Patterns" Portfolio*
   - Students write cover letters and assemble portfolios for the unit

At Home

Students prepare for unit assessments

Discuss With Your Colleagues

Portfolio Expectations

Portfolios are probably new for your students, and perhaps for you as well. Discuss with your colleagues what you want from students for the various parts of the *Patterns* portfolio, and what your level of expectation is.

You may also want to discuss how you will assess the portfolios and what role they should play in students' grades.

1. Reminder: Unit Assessments Tomorrow

You should alert students to the fact that they will have their final assessments for the unit tomorrow and tomorrow night. You may want to describe the structure of the assessment, which has an in-class portion and a take-home portion (see tomorrow's discussion).

2. Discussion of *Homework 23: Cutting Through the Layers*

Have the students, in their groups, agree on a rule for the number of pieces. As they do this, you can circulate to check that all groups were able to find the general rule. If some groups did not, you can ask groups who solved the problem to give hints to those who did not.

"Can you think of a good hint for another group?"

Some students may have thought about why the number of pieces should be given by the rule $LC + 1$. If enough students seem interested, you can discuss this, or you can recommend that students look at the supplemental problem *Explaining the Layers*.

3. *"Patterns" Portfolio*

(see facing page)

"What are portfolios and what should go into them?"

Before students begin work on their portfolios, you may want to ask them what they recall about portfolios from the discussion at the beginning of the unit. You can ask specific questions, such as

- What is the purpose of a portfolio?
- What would be good items to include in a portfolio?

After this brief review of portfolios in general, tell students to read *"Patterns" Portfolio* carefully.

You may wish to lead a general review discussion about the unit before students begin work on their cover letters, or you may prefer to let students work in groups or on their own.

The selection of portfolio materials and the writing of cover letters are intertwined activities. Students should probably at least begin their general review of the unit before selecting portfolio materials, but they will need to make certain selections in order to complete the cover letters. The "personal growth" portion of the portfolio can be completed last.

As students read through the unit and look over their work, they should think about both the mathematical content of the unit and the quality of their writing. They should choose work that conveys the essence of the unit

"Patterns" Portfolio

Now that *Patterns* is completed, it is time to put together your portfolio for the unit. Compiling this portfolio has three parts:

- Writing a cover letter in which you summarize the unit
- Choosing papers to include from your work in the unit
- Discussing your personal growth during the unit

Cover Letter for Patterns

Look back over *Patterns* and write a cover letter describing the central ideas of the unit. This description should include

- mathematical concepts
- ideas about what mathematics is and how mathematics is learned
- any other general themes of the unit

As part of the compilation of your portfolio, you will select activities both about In-Out tables and about angles. Your cover letter should include an explanation of why you select the particular items you do.

Selecting Papers from Patterns

Look through all of your papers for *Patterns,* and select the items described below for your portfolio.

- *Homework 1: Past Experiences*

  Include this so you can look back later and compare your experiences before this year to your experiences with the Interactive Mathematics Program.

- One or two activities on In-Out tables

  Choose activities that helped you understand what In-Out tables are and how to use them.

- *Homework 14: You're the Chef*

  You will be asked to refer to this summary of the hot-and-cold-cube model in Year 2 of the Interactive Mathematics Program.

Continued on next page

as well as work that illustrates their expertise in solving and writing about problems.

Tell students that they will be able to refer to their portfolios when they work on unit assessments (including tomorrow's) and will sometimes use them when later units build on earlier ones.

You may want to let students complete the *Patterns* portfolio for homework. Be sure that they bring the portfolio back tomorrow with the cover letter as the first item. They should also bring any other work that they think will

- One or two activities about angles

  Choose activities that strengthened your understanding of angles or that gave you new insight into angles and polygons.

- A Problem of the Week

  Select one of the three POWs you completed during this unit *(The Broken Eggs, 1-2-3-4 Puzzle,* or *Checkerboard Squares).* Choose a POW in which you explained your thought processes well, perhaps used several different strategies, and so on.

- Other quality work

  Select one or two other pieces of work that demonstrate your best efforts. (These can be any work from the unit, such as a Problem of the Week, homework, classwork, or presentation.)

Later you'll add the in-class and take-home assessments for *Patterns.*

Personal Growth

Your cover letter for *Patterns* describes how the unit develops. As part of your portfolio, write about your personal development during this unit. You may want to address the questions below.

✓ How do you feel you progressed

- in working together with others?
- in presenting to the class?
- in writing about and describing your thought processes?

✓ What do you feel you need to work on and how might you work on it?

You should include here any other thoughts about your experience with this unit that you want to share with a reader of your portfolio.

help them on tomorrow's unit assessments. They can keep the remainder of their work at home.

Homework: Prepare for Assessments

Students' homework for tonight is to prepare for tomorrow's assessments by reviewing the ideas of the unit.

DAY 25 Final Assessments

Students do the in-class assessment and can begin the take-home assessment.

Outline of the Day

In Class

Introduce assessments

- Students do *In-Class Assessment for "Patterns"*
- Students begin *Take-Home Assessment for "Patterns"*

At Home

Students complete *Take-Home Assessment for "Patterns"*

Special Materials Needed

- *In-Class Assessment for "Patterns"*
- *Take-Home Assessment for "Patterns"*

End-of-Unit Assessments

Note: The in-class portions of unit assessments are intentionally short so that time pressure will not be a factor in students' ability to do well. The IMP *Teaching Handbook* contains further general information about the purpose of the end-of-unit assessments and how to use them.

Tell students that today they will get two tests—one that they will finish in class and one that they can start in class and finish at home. The take-home part should be handed in tomorrow.

Tell students that they are allowed to use graphing calculators, pattern blocks, protractors, notes from previous work, and so forth, when they do the assessments. (They will have to do without graphing calculators on the take-home portion unless they have their own.)

These assessments are provided separately in Appendix B for you to duplicate.

In-Class Assessment for "Patterns"

1. Explain each of the following problems in terms of the model of hot and cold cubes. Your explanation should include a statement of how the temperature changes overall in each case.

   a. 3 - (-2)

   b. 5 • (-4)

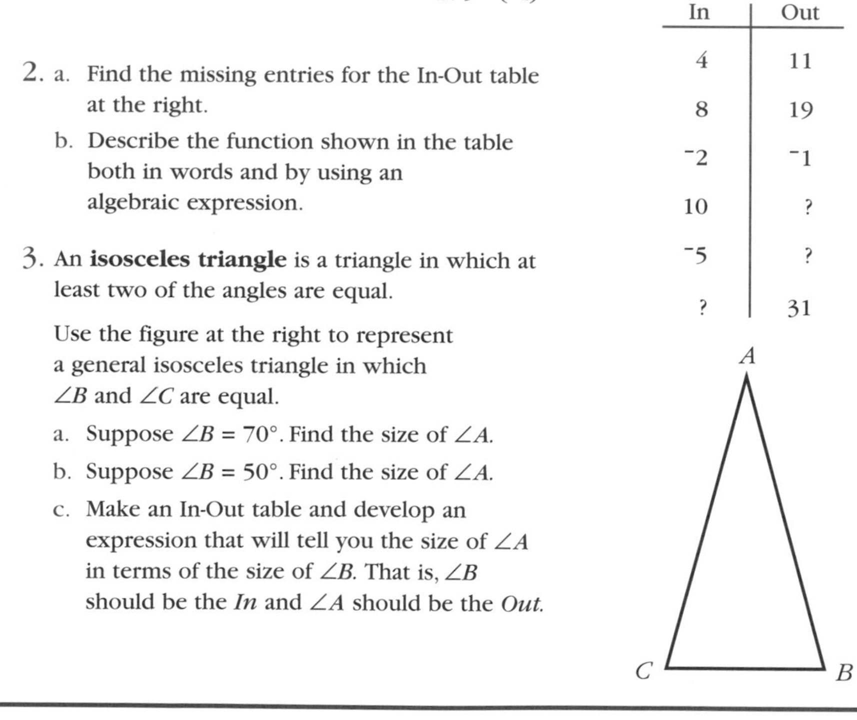

In	Out
4	11
8	19
$^{-}2$	$^{-}1$
10	?
$^{-}5$	?
?	31

2. a. Find the missing entries for the In-Out table at the right.

   b. Describe the function shown in the table both in words and by using an algebraic expression.

3. An **isosceles triangle** is a triangle in which at least two of the angles are equal.

   Use the figure at the right to represent a general isosceles triangle in which $\angle B$ and $\angle C$ are equal.

   a. Suppose $\angle B = 70°$. Find the size of $\angle A$.

   b. Suppose $\angle B = 50°$. Find the size of $\angle A$.

   c. Make an In-Out table and develop an expression that will tell you the size of $\angle A$ in terms of the size of $\angle B$. That is, $\angle B$ should be the *In* and $\angle A$ should be the *Out.*

Take-Home Assessment for *Patterns*

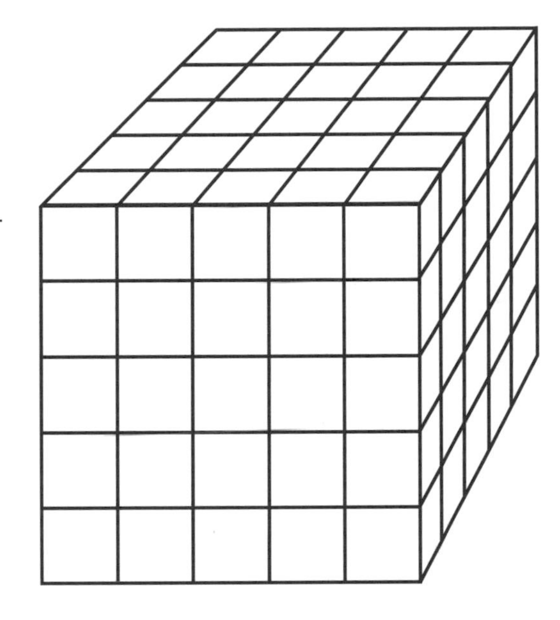

This problem is like the border problem, but it involves cubes instead of squares.

Imagine that you have a cube that is 5 inches long on every side. This large cube is made up of smaller cubes, and each small cube is 1 inch on every side.

Someone comes along and paints the large cube on all of its faces, including the bottom. None of the paint leaks to the inside.

How many of the smaller cubes have any paint at all on them? (Careful! The answer is neither 125 nor 150.)

How many of the smaller cubes have just one face painted?

How many have two faces painted?

Answer the same question for three, four, five, and six faces.

Your write-up for this problem should include

- *Problem Statement:* Restate the problem in your own words.
- *Process:* Please show all the work you did in solving this problem. If you used diagrams or tables, include them.
- *Solution:* Give your solution and justify it so that someone else will be convinced that your solution is correct.

Homework: Complete *Take-Home Assessments for "Patterns"*

Students should bring back the completed assessment tomorrow. As with all work done at home, students may collaborate or get assistance, but they should report this as part of their write-up of the assessment.

Summing Up

Students sum up what they learned in the unit.

Mathematical Topics

- Summarizing the unit

Outline of the Day

1. Discuss unit assessments
2. Sum up the unit

Note: The assessment discussions and unit summary are presented as if they take place on the day following the assessments, but you may prefer to delay this material until you have looked over students' work on the assessments.

These discussion ideas are included here as their own "day" to remind you that some time should be allotted for such a discussion.

Discuss With Your Colleagues

Working with Variables

Students get many experiences in this unit using variables to express generalizations.

Is this algebra? Or is algebra the manipulation of symbols, such as multiplying polynomials or solving quadratic equations?

For many students who fail traditional algebra classes, the big problem is that they have no idea what the variables are all about. Discuss how the gradual introduction of variables in *Patterns* takes the mystery out of x and y.

1. Discussion of Unit Assessments

You can have students volunteer to explain their work on each of the problems. Encourage questions and alternate explanations from other students.

- *In-class assessment*

You can use Question 1 to review the way the hot-and-cold-cube model works.

On Question 2, you may want to focus on how students found their pattern for the table.

On Question 3, you can emphasize the way several different ideas come together in this problem, including the technique of working with specific cases, the use of In-Out tables, and the rule for the sum of the angles of a triangle.

- *Take-home assessment*

There are several different questions within the take-home assessment, and you can have different students present their ideas for each question.

Note: A supplemental problem, *Painting the General Cube* (in *The Overland Trail,* later in Year 1), asks students to generalize this problem.

2. Unit Summary

Let volunteers share their portfolio cover letters as a way to start a discussion to summarize the unit.

"What have you learned in this unit?"

Then let them brainstorm to come up with descriptions of what they have learned in the unit. This is a good opportunity to review terminology and to place the unit in a broader mathematics context.

Some in the class may think that students in a traditional curriculum are busy learning algebra formulas and the like, and may feel that they are missing out on something. You may want to have them do a "reality check" and find out what students in an algebra course have learned in the first six weeks or so. If there are specific topics they are concerned about, you can let them know when those topics will be discussed in the IMP curriculum. (The IMP *Teaching Handbook* includes a unit-by-unit outline of the curriculum.)

Use this occasion to talk about the integrated nature of the IMP curriculum, so students realize that they will be learning a mixture of things in each unit. For example, they have probably learned more about geometry than most students in a traditional algebra course. They have also done more writing, explaining, problem solving, and working with proofs than those students.

You can also point out that they have done a lot of work with what is perhaps the most important single idea in algebra—the use of variables to express generalizations. You might have them list a few examples of general principles that they have developed.

Supplemental Problems

This appendix contains a variety of additional activities that you can use to supplement the unit material. These activities are included at the end of the student materials and fall roughly into two categories.

- Reinforcements, which increase students' understanding and comfort with concepts, techniques, and methods that are discussed in class and that are central to the unit
- Extensions, which allow students to explore ideas beyond the basic unit, sometimes dealing with generalizations or abstractions of ideas that are part of the main unit

The supplemental activities are listed here in the approximate sequence in which you might use them in the unit. (They appear in the same order in the student materials.)

This appendix includes specific recommendations about how each activity might work within the unit. You may wish to use some of these activities, especially the later ones, after the unit is completed.

For more ideas about the use of supplemental activities in the IMP curriculum, see the IMP *Teaching Handbook*.

- *Whose Dog Is That?* (extension)

  You can assign this problem any time after the discussion of *Homework 2: Who's Who?* Its purpose is to give students another opportunity for organized thinking and for writing clear explanations. Emphasize that students must not only give the names of each woman's husband and each woman's dog, but must demonstrate clearly how they know that there are no other answers.

  This problem is more complex than *Homework 2: Who's Who?*, so you should give students several days to work on it and to write up their results.

- *A Fractional Life* (reinforcement)

  Students will most likely approach this ancient problem with a guess-and-check method, and it therefore can be used to reinforce their work with In-Out tables. It can best be used after you introduce In-Out tables on Day 5.

- *Infinite Proof* (extension)

  This problem is a follow-up to students' work on *Homework 6: Gettin' On Down to One*. In the discussion of that problem, students are told that there is, to date, no proof that every sequence generated by the pattern described must eventually get to 1.

  They may believe that no proof exists simply because there are infinitely many cases to check. This activity gives them the experience of seeing that proofs are possible for situations involving infinitely many cases. (They will see other such proofs in *Homework 12: That's Odd!* and in their work with angle sums.)

- *It's All Gone* (reinforcement)

  As with *Marcella's Bagels*, this problem can perhaps best be solved by working backwards. You can use it any time after the discussion of *Marcella's Bagels* on Day 7.

- *More Broken Eggs* (extension)

  This problem asks students to look for more solutions to *POW 1: The Broken Eggs*. You can assign it any time after the discussion of *POW 1: The Broken Eggs* on Day 9.

- *The Number Magician* (reinforcement)

  You can think of this problem as describing a multistep In-Out machine. It might be most appropriate after students get some experience looking for rules, perhaps after *Homework 10: Pulling Out Rules*.

- *Three in a Row* (extension)

  Three in a Row is an extension of the ideas that students used and discussed in connection with *Homework 12: That's Odd!* You can assign it any time after the discussion of that homework.

- *Any Old Sum* (reinforcement or extension)

  This activity is a variation on the *Consecutive Sums* investigation. There is a simple pattern for the total number of ways to write a given number. You can suggest to students that they look for other patterns besides this one, and also that they look for explanations of their patterns. You can assign *Any Old Sum* any time after the *Consecutive Sums* activity is completed on Day 13, and you can give students several days to work on it.

  Although the content of this activity is an extension of ideas in the main unit, the activity is a reinforcement in that it gives students more experience in exploring an open-ended problem.

- *Getting Involved*

  This reflection on group process might fit well after the *Consecutive Sums* work. (Since this activity has a nonmathematical focus, it is not categorized as either reinforcement or extension.)

- ***Chef Divisions*** (reinforcement or extension)

  Although *Chef Divisions* extends the ideas introduced through the hot-and-cold-cubes model, its main purpose is to get students to think further about the model and the reasoning involved in using negative numbers. It will also force them to think about the meaning of division. You can use it any time after *Homework 14: You're the Chef.*

- ***1-2-3-4 Varieties*** (reinforcement)

  You can assign this at any time after the discussion of *POW 2: 1-2-3-4 Expressions* on Day 15.

- ***The General Theory of Consecutive Sums*** (extension)

  You can assign this follow-up to *Consecutive Sums* any time after students seem comfortable with the arithmetic of integers (for example, after Day 15). It is a challenging assignment, and you should allow students several days to work on it.

- ***Instruct the Pro*** (reinforcement)

  This activity is designed for students who have had little or no experience with protractors prior to this unit. You can use it as a follow-up to *A Protracted Engagement* (Day 17), perhaps as a homework assignment that night so that students get more experience with protractors before *Degree Discovery*.

- ***Diagonals Illuminated*** (extension)

  This problem poses two ways to follow up on *Homework 17: Diagonally Speaking,* and you can assign it any time after the discussion of that homework.

  Question 1 is primarily a question about the In-Out table, rather than about diagonals. That is, it asks students to work from their table to get a closed formula. Question 2 essentially asks students to prove their general method for counting diagonals, whether they use a summation process or a closed formula.

- ***From Another Angle*** (extension)

  This activity is most appropriate following *Homework 19: An Angular Summary*. In fact, Question 1 of *From Another Angle* is essentially a generalization of Question 2a in that homework.

  Students will benefit from having actual pattern blocks to work with on Question 2 of this problem. Part b of Question 2 is the most challenging section.

- ***Lots of Squares*** (extension)

  A challenging problem involving both geometry and number patterns, *Lots of Squares* calls for a proof from students. Therefore, you should probably assign it after they have done most of the work on proofs in the unit, including *Homework 12: That's Odd!* and *A Proof Gone Bad* (Day 19).

- *From One to N* (extension)

  This problem is a natural outgrowth of *Homework 20: Squares and Scoops* and can be used after discussion of that assignment.

- *Different Kinds of Checkerboards* (extension)

  You can use this problem any time after the discussion of *POW 3: Checkerboard Squares* on Day 21.

- *Programming Down to One* (extension)

  This problem will require a great deal of independent work by the student in learning some programming fundamentals, including screen display and the use of "if" statements. It can be used any time after Day 22 and is offered primarily for students who are enchanted with the technology of the calculator.

- *More About Borders* (extension)

  This problem is a follow-up to *Homework 22: Border Varieties*.

- *Programming Borders* (reinforcement)

  This problem involves programming at a level similar to that used on Days 22 and 23, but builds on work in the supplemental problem *More About Borders*. Students can work on this problem at different levels of complexity, depending on their work on *More About Borders*.

  This activity is labeled a reinforcement because its main purpose is to strengthen understanding of programming, even though the content involves ideas in the extension problem, *More About Borders*.

- *Explaining the Layers* (extension)

  This problem is a follow-up to *Homework 23: Cutting Through the Layers* and asks students to prove the formula developed in that activity.

Appendix

Supplemental Problems

This page in the student book introduces the supplemental problems.

The supplemental problems for each unit pursue some of the themes and ideas that are important in that unit.

Here are some examples from the supplemental problems for *Patterns.*

- *Whose Dog is That?* and *Infinite Proof* continue your work with proof.
- *Three in a Row* and *The General Theory of Consecutive Sums* follow up on your investigation of consecutive sums.
- *Instruct the Pro* and *From Another Angle* give you more experience measuring and thinking about angles.

Other supplemental problems for *Patterns* follow up on concepts and techniques for working with In-Out tables, integers, and calculator programming.

Whose Dog Is That?

Abigail, Bertha, Candy, Dodi, and Eudora showed up with their puppies at the Little Red School House for Dogs. During the morning break, they found that each of their pets has the same name as the husband of one of the other women.

In particular, they noticed that

- Abigail's dog is named George.
- Candy's dog is named Jerry.
- Eudora's dog is named Ike.
- Dodi's dog is named Frank.
- Abigail's husband is also named Frank.
- Bertha's husband has the same name as George's dog.
- Horace and his wife, Candy, have the best behaved dog.

Your job is to figure out the names of each woman's husband and each woman's dog.

In addition, you must explain clearly how you found your answer. If you think there is more than one possibility, give all solutions, and explain why there are no more. If you think there is only one solution, explain why there are no others.

A Fractional Life

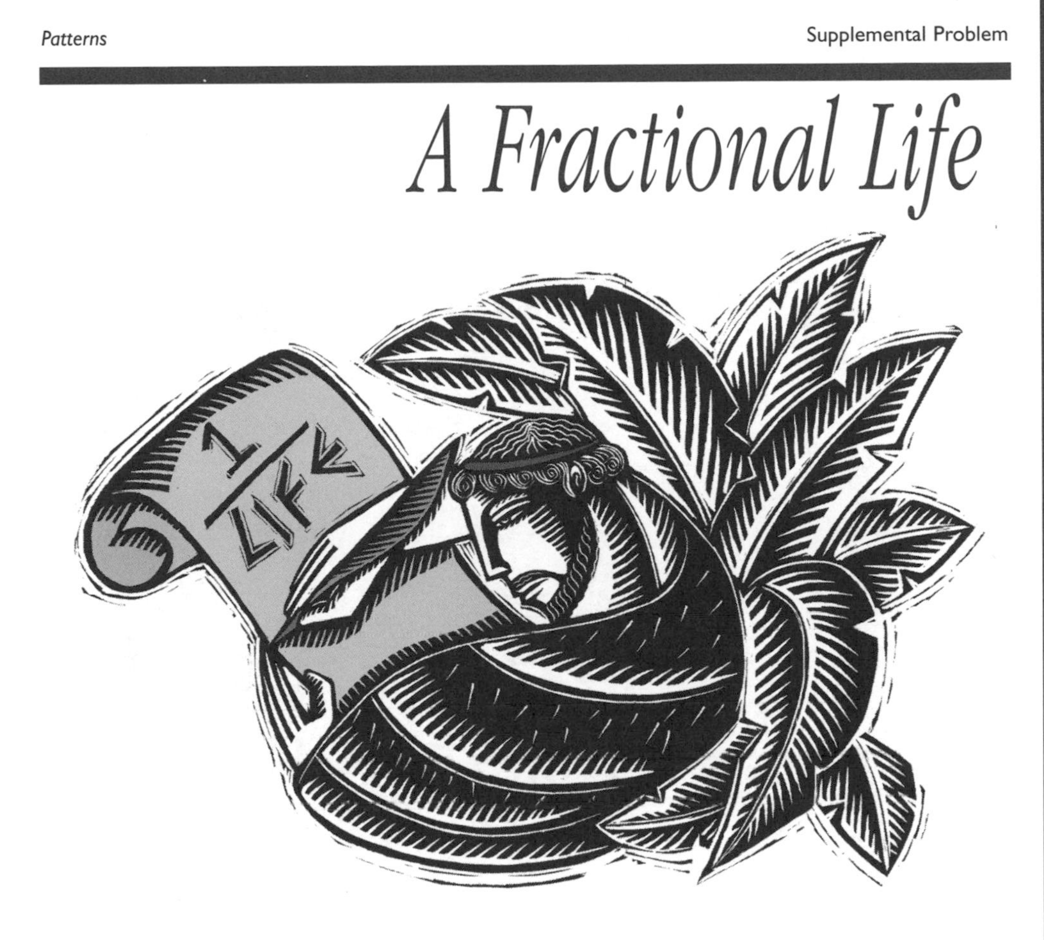

Here is a problem that is part of *The Greek Anthology*, a group of problems collected by ancient Greek mathematicians.

> Demochares has lived a fourth of his life as a boy, a fifth as a youth, a third as a man, and has spent 13 years in his dotage. How old is he?
>
> *How old is Demochares?*

(*Note:* The phrase "in his dotage" refers to the period of Demochares' old age.)

Infinite Proof

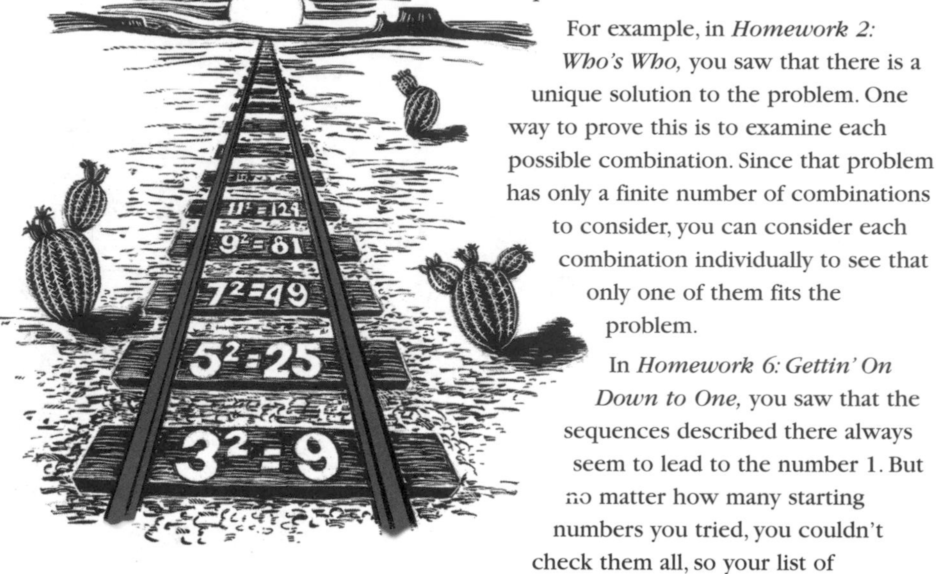

Proof involves considering all the possible cases.

For example, in *Homework 2: Who's Who,* you saw that there is a unique solution to the problem. One way to prove this is to examine each possible combination. Since that problem has only a finite number of combinations to consider, you can consider each combination individually to see that only one of them fits the problem.

In *Homework 6: Gettin' On Down to One,* you saw that the sequences described there always seem to lead to the number 1. But no matter how many starting numbers you tried, you couldn't check them all, so your list of examples was not a proof. In fact, no one has ever proved that you "get down to 1" for every possible starting number.

This problem is about proving things about every possible case in situations where there are infinitely many cases to consider.

1. You know that there are infinitely many odd numbers. Prove that the square of *every* odd number is odd.

2. A **prime number** is a number greater than 1 whose only whole number divisors are 1 and itself. For example, 3 and 7 are both prime numbers. But 12 is not a prime number, since it has whole number divisors other than 1 and 12. For example, 4 is a divisor of 12.

   Prove that *every* prime number greater than 10 must have the digit 1, 3, 7, or 9 in the ones column.

It's All Gone

A man goes into a store and says, "If you give me as much money as I have with me now, I will spend $10 in your store." The proprietor agrees, and the man spends the money.

He goes into a second store and again says, "If you give me as much money as I have with me now, I will spend $10 in your store." Again, the proprietor agrees, and the man spends the money.

In a third store, he repeats his proposition, the proprietor agrees, and the man spends the money.

At this point, the man has no money left.

How much money did this man have to begin with? Explain your answer.

More Broken Eggs

In *POW 1: The Broken Eggs,* you found a possible number of eggs that the farmer might have had when her cart was knocked over.

You may have found only one solution to that problem, but there are actually many solutions.

Your task is to look for other solutions to the problem. Find as many as you can. If possible, find and describe a pattern for getting all the solutions and explain why all solutions fit your pattern.

Here are the facts you need to know.

- When the farmer put the eggs in groups of two, there was one egg left over.
- When she put them in groups of three, there was also one egg left over. The same thing happened when she put them in groups of four, five, or six.
- When she put the eggs in groups of seven, she ended up with complete groups of seven with no eggs left over.

The Number Magician

A magician said to a volunteer from the audience, "Pick a number, but don't tell me what it is. Add 15 to it. Multiply your answer by 3. Subtract 9. Divide by 3. Subtract 8. Now tell me your answer."

"Thirty-two," replied the volunteer.

Then the magician *immediately* guessed the number that the volunteer had originally chosen.

1. What was the volunteer's number?
2. How did the magician know so quickly? (The magician couldn't possibly have worked backwards that fast.)

Three in a Row

In *Homework 12: That's Odd!* you looked at the conjecture that any odd number greater than 1 can be written as a sum of two consecutive natural numbers.

In this problem, you are to examine what kinds of numbers can be written as a sum of *three* consecutive natural numbers.

1. Try to come up with a simple description of such numbers.
2. Once you come up with a conjecture on how to describe such numbers, try to prove your conjecture.

   Note: Your proof might have two parts—the first showing that all numbers that fit your description *can* be written as such a sum, and the second showing that all numbers that can be written as such a sum *fit* your description.
3. Look for a generalization that holds for sums of other lengths and try to prove it. *Suggestion:* Start by looking at sums for another odd number of terms. You may want to consider consecutive sums of *integers,* and not restrict yourself to natural numbers.

Any Old Sum

This problem, like *Consecutive Sums,* is about sums of natural numbers, that is, sums of whole numbers other than zero.

But this time you aren't restricted to consecutive sums. Now your task is to look at *all* the ways various numbers can be written as a sum of natural numbers.

For example, the number 4 can be written in exactly eight ways, as shown below.

1 + 1 + 1 + 1	1 + 2 + 1
2 + 2	4
2 + 1 + 1	3 + 1
1 + 3	1 + 1 + 2

Notice that 4 by itself is counted as a way, and that 1 + 2 + 1, 2 + 1 + 1, and 1 + 1 + 2 are all counted separately.

Explore. Look for patterns. Look at ways of categorizing the different ways to write a number as a sum. Make some generalizations.

State each generalization clearly and try to explain why that generalization is always true.

Getting Involved

Imagine that you have been in the same group for about a week. During that time, everyone in your group has been doing fine except one person.

This person doesn't say a thing besides "I don't know" and won't help with presentations.

Write about

- why someone might behave that way
- what you and the group can do about it

Be specific and look for many possibilities.

Chef Divisions

Nowhere in the Chef's Manual is there any reference to hot and cold cubes and the division of negative numbers.

For example, what would the chefs mean by the expression $15 \div -3$? What might the numbers 15 or -3 in this division problem represent in terms of the hot-and-cold-cube model?

1. Explain this specific problem in terms of the model.
2. Make up some other division problems using integers and explain them using the model. Include different combinations of signs.
3. Suppose a and b were arbitrary integers. Give a general description of what an expression of the form $a \div b$ would mean. What would a tell you? What would b tell you?

1-2-3-4 Varieties

In *POW 2: 1-2-3-4 Puzzle,* you were asked to express each of the numbers from 1 to 25 as a 1-2-3-4 expression.

As you may recall, a 1-2-3-4 expression is an arithmetic expression that uses each of the digits 1, 2, 3, and 4 exactly once, according to certain rules.

Your task in this problem is to do the assignment again but with one additional rule.

- The digits 1, 2, 3, and 4 must appear in order.

For example, you can express the number 10 as $1 + 2 + 3 + 4$, but not as $4 \cdot 3 - 2 \cdot 1$ or as $3 + 2 + 1 + 4$.

Are all results from 1 through 25 still possible? What is the highest result you can get?

What other problems can you make up that are variations of this POW?

The General Theory of Consecutive Sums

In the activity *Consecutive Sums,* you were restricted to positive whole numbers (1, 2, 3, 4, etc.).

But the idea of consecutive sums also makes sense for all integers. For example, "-2 + -1 + 0 + 1" is a consecutive sum for the number -2.

Your task in this activity is to investigate how your results on *Consecutive Sums* would have been different if you had been allowed to use the complete set of integers—positive, negative, and zero. (You can use the hot-and-cold-cube model to help with the arithmetic of the sums.)

In particular, you may want to look for a general rule for the number of ways in which a given integer can be expressed as a consecutive sum.

If you worked on the problem *Three in a Row,* you may find your results from that problem helpful.

Start with lots of examples. Look for patterns in your data and then think about ways in which you might explain those patterns.

Supplemental Problem

Patterns

Instruct the Pro

Take a clean sheet of paper and make a sketch of something made up only of line segments touching end to end, like the one at the right. (Your sketch can be more interesting than this one.)

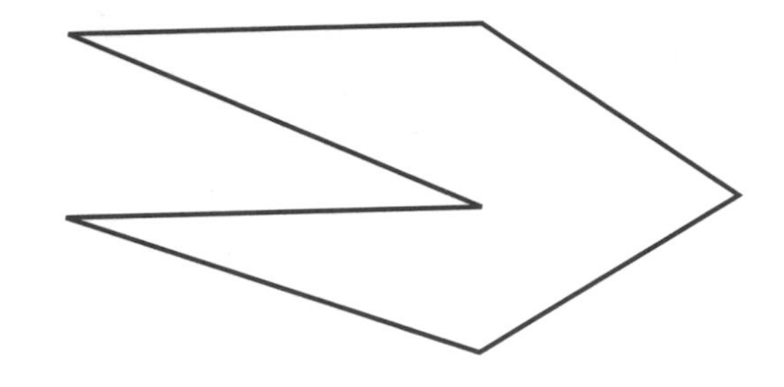

Then write instructions so that someone with a ruler and protractor could draw a diagram exactly like yours without seeing your diagram.

Suggestion: Select a point in your diagram where two segments meet, and use that point as the starting point for your instructions. You may also want to tell the person where to start on the sheet of paper. For example, you might say, "Start in the center of your page."

Diagonals Illuminated

In *Homework 17: Diagonally Speaking,* you looked at a pattern for finding the number of diagonals of a polygon.

The goal of that problem was to find a way to get the number of diagonals as a function of the number of sides of the polygon.

This activity provides two further investigations you can do to gain more insight about diagonals. The two investigations are somewhat independent of each other—you can work on one without working on the other—but your work on either problem might help you understand the remaining one.

These investigations involve some general ideas that have nothing to do with diagonals.

Continued on next page

To get a sense of these ideas, suppose you are using an In-Out table to solve the following simple problem:

A group of people are in a room. How many hands do they have?

If you make a table in which the *Ins* increase by 1 at each step, you might notice that the *Outs* are going up by 2 at each step. You can explain this pattern by the fact that when another person joins the group, two more hands are added.

In other words, the number of hands for $n + 1$ people is 2 more than the number of hands for n people. In this approach, each table entry is found from the previous one. This type of description of an In-Out table is called a **recursive function.**

On the other hand, you might look at the table and notice that each *Out* is exactly twice the corresponding *In*. You can explain this by the fact that each person has two hands.

In other words, the table can be described by the formula $Out = 2 \cdot In$. In this approach, the *Out* is expressed directly in terms of the *In*. A formula like this is called a *closed formula.*

Now use the ideas of *recursive function* and *closed formula* in these problems.

1. You may have found a recursive function for the number of diagonals in a polygon, in which you described how the number of diagonals grows as the number of sides increases by one side at a time. But a recursive function can be difficult to work with if the polygon has many sides.

   For example, you probably wouldn't want to use a recursive function to find the number of diagonals for a 1000-sided polygon.

   Your task in this problem is to find a closed formula for the In-Out table from *Homework 17: Diagonally Speaking.* That is, look for a formula that will allow you to find the number of diagonals for *any* polygon directly in terms of the number of sides, without having to work your way through all the cases of polygons with fewer sides.

2. Whatever method you discovered for finding the number of diagonals, you probably found it by looking at some examples and seeing a pattern.

   That's an excellent approach, but it doesn't necessarily tell you *why* the pattern holds. If you aren't sure why it holds, then you don't have much of a guarantee that the pattern *always* holds.

   Your task in this problem is to *explain* why your method for finding the number of diagonals must work. Whether you are using a *recursive function* or a *closed formula,* you will need to think about what a diagonal is and not just look at the numerical pattern of your data.

From Another Angle

As you saw in *Homework 19: An Angular Summary,* a regular polygon is a polygon in which all the angles are equal and the sides are equal.

For example, the three pattern blocks shown at the left are in the shape of regular polygons.

The problems below involve both pattern blocks and regular polygons. In doing these problems, you may use any formulas you know for the sum of the angles of a polygon.

1. Make an In-Out table where the *In* is the number of sides of a regular polygon and the *Out* is the size of each angle of such a polygon.

   For example, if a regular polygon has three sides, each angle of that polygon is 60°, since the three angles must add up to 180°.

   Look for a rule for your table.

2. Investigate whether any other regular polygons, besides those shown above, can be made from pattern blocks.

   a. For each polygon that can be made, draw a picture to show how it can be made.

   b. Explain why your answer to part a is complete. That is, explain why no other regular polygons can be made.

   (Careful! One polygon that can be made has more than six sides.)

You may want to use pattern blocks to do this assignment. For your convenience, pictures of all six pattern blocks are shown here.

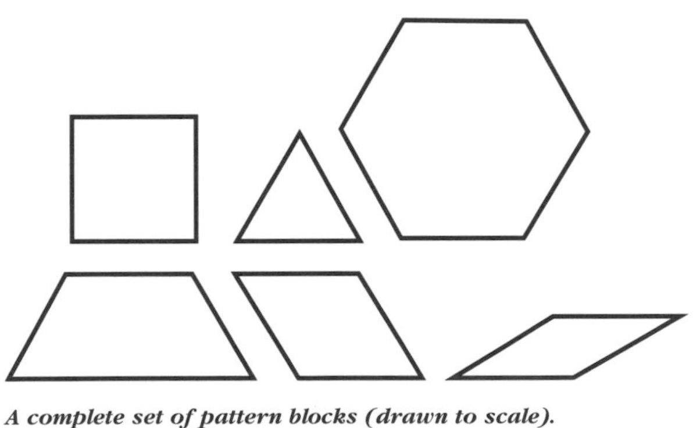

A complete set of pattern blocks (drawn to scale).

Lots of Squares

Can you divide a square into a certain number of smaller squares? That may depend on exactly how many smaller squares you want.

The first diagram at the right shows that any square can be divided into four smaller squares. The second diagram shows that any square can be divided into seven smaller squares.

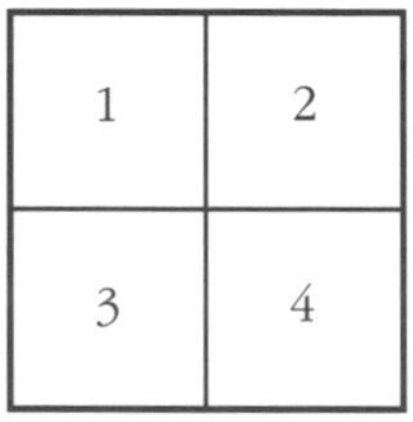

1	2
3	4

1	2, 3, 4, 5
6	7

Notice that these smaller squares don't have to be the same size as each other, but keep in mind that the smaller portions must all be squares, not simply rectangles.

The task of this activity is to investigate what numbers of smaller squares are possible. For example, you can probably see that there is no way to divide a square into just two smaller squares. (Try it and convince yourself that it's impossible.)

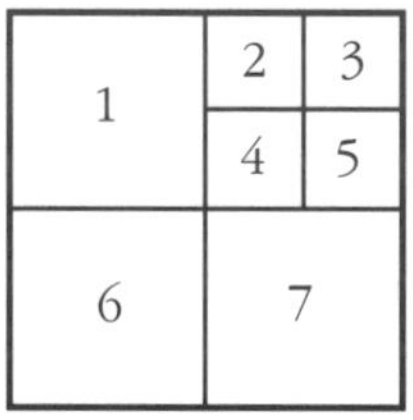

1. Start with specific cases. Is it possible to divide a square into three smaller squares? Five? Six? Eight? (The cases of four and seven smaller squares are shown in the diagrams, although you may want to look for other ways to do them.)

   Continue this process, at least up to the case of 13 smaller squares.

Now reflect on what you've done, and just *imagine* continuing this process. Would there be any numbers beyond 13 for which you *couldn't* divide a square into that many smaller squares? What patterns can you find in the cases you've done that help with this question?

2. a. What is the largest "impossible" case?

   b. Prove your answer to Question 2a. That is, prove that all cases beyond the one you named in Question 2a are possible.

From One to N

In Question 1 of *Homework 20: Squares and Scoops,* you looked at the number of squares in an "n-high" stack.

You may have seen that this number could be found by getting the sum $1 + 2 + \cdots + n$. For example, the number of squares in a 5-high stack is $1 + 2 + 3 + 4 + 5$.

The sum $1 + 2 + \cdots + n$ occurs often in mathematics problems. (You may have used a similar sum in *Homework 17: Diagonally Speaking.*)

Your task in this activity is to find a simple expression in terms of n that allows you to find this sum without repeated addition. (What you are looking for is called a *closed formula,* as explained in the problem *Diagonals Illuminated.*)

If you find such an expression, look for a proof that your answer is correct. Don't just say, "It works"; you need to guarantee that it works for *every* value of n.

Different Kinds of Checkerboards

In *POW 3: Checkerboard Squares,* you found a way to compute the total number of squares that can be formed as a combination of squares on an n-by-n checkerboard.

But what if the checkerboard itself isn't necessarily square? For example, how many squares are there altogether on the 4-by-6 checkerboard shown at the left?

Here are two examples of squares that can be formed on that checkerboard.

Start with this 4-by-6 example, and then look for ways to generalize what you find.

Your goal is to find a method to compute the total number of squares that can be formed from squares on an m-by-n checkerboard.

Programming Down to One

In *Homework 6: Gettin' On Down to One,* you examined a process for generating sequences of numbers. Here's a summary of that process.

You begin with a starting number. You find each number after that by applying one of two rules to the current number.

The decision about which rule to apply depends on whether the current number is odd or even.

- If the current number is odd, the rule is

  Multiply the current number by 3 and then add 1 to get the next number.

- If the current number is even, the rule is

  Divide the current number by 2 to get the next number.

The task in this assignment is to write a program that will generate the sequence for you.

There are several types of programs that you could write for this task. Here are three possibilities.

Continued on next page

Option 1

The program asks the user for a number, and then tells the user what the next number is.

For example, the screen for such a program might look like the display at the right.

The user of the program enters the number 13. The program does the rest.

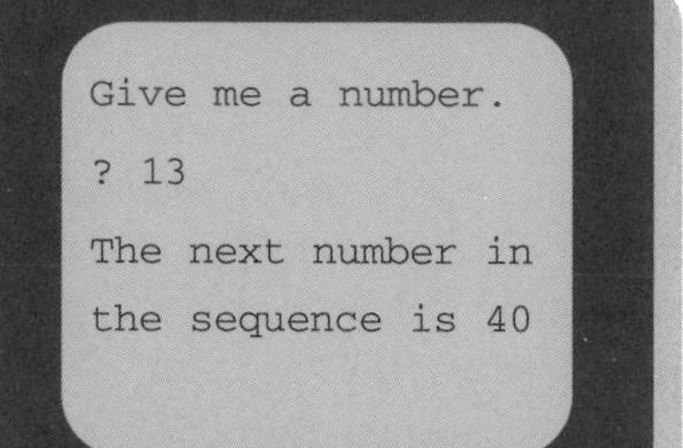

Option 2

The program asks the user for a number, and then generates a sequence of terms based on the two rules.

For example, the screen for such a program might look like the display at the right.

Again, everything except the number 13 following the question mark is done by the program.

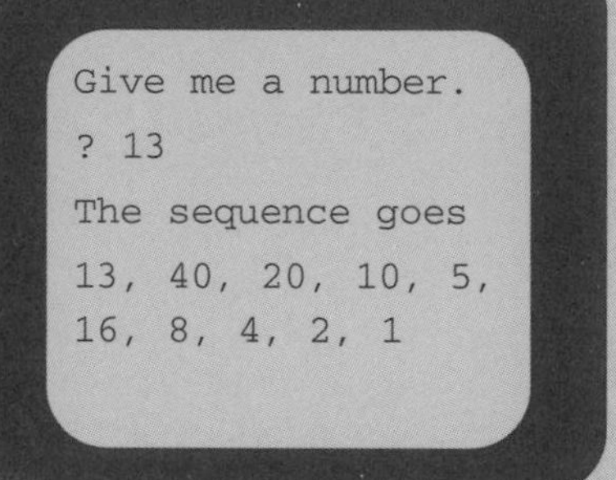

Option 3

The program asks the user for a number, and then tells the user how many steps it takes to get to 1, without actually showing the terms.

For example, the screen for such a program might look like the display at the right.

Again, everything except the number 13 following the question mark is done by the program.

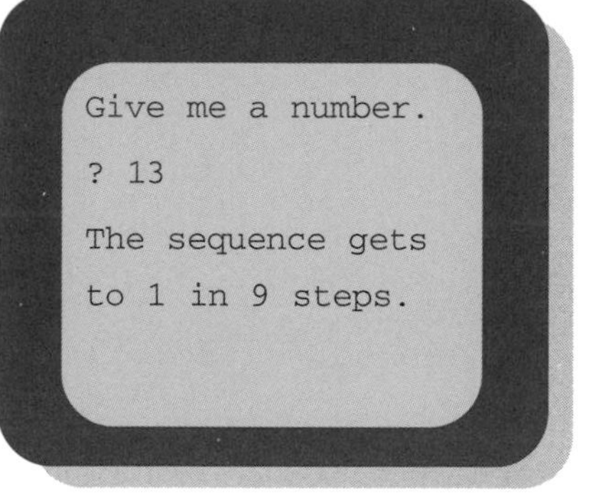

Whatever option or options you work on, your program will have to determine which of the two rules to use, depending on whether a given number is odd or even.

You may want to consult a manual to find out how to display words on the screen, how to put the decision about which rule to use into your program, and so on.

More About Borders

The problem in *Homework 22: Border Varieties* involved finding the number of tiles needed to form a border around an s-by-s square.

In this activity, you will explore some variations or extensions of that problem.

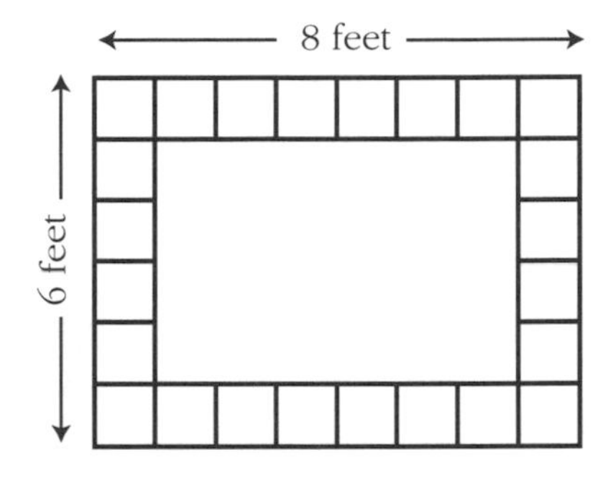

1. Suppose Leslie's garden isn't square. For example, if she has a garden that is 6 feet by 8 feet, the tiles would look like the diagram at the right.

   Explore examples like this, and then develop an expression for the number of tiles needed for the border of a garden that is m feet by n feet.

2. Suppose that each tile costs \$3. Suppose also that Leslie buys topsoil for the part of the garden that is not tiled, and it costs 20¢ for each square foot of ground to be covered with topsoil.

   Develop an expression in terms of m and n for Leslie's total cost for tiles and topsoil for a garden that is m feet by n feet.

3. Consider the problem of creating a border 2 feet wide. For example, for a garden 10 feet by 10 feet, the border would look like the diagram at the right.

   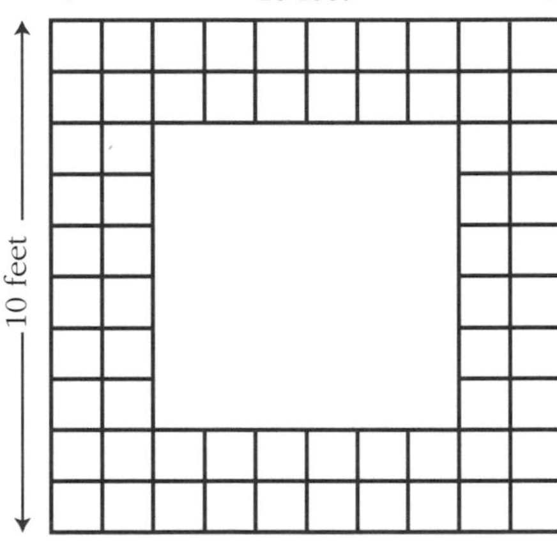

   How many tiles would be needed?

   And, in general, how many tiles would be needed for a border like this for a square garden that is s feet by s feet? And what about for a rectangular garden that is m feet by n feet?

   And what would Leslie's costs be, based on the information in Question 2?

4. Generalize the problem even further by considering a border that is r feet wide all around.

Supplemental Problem
Patterns

Programming Borders

```
How wide is the
garden?
? 7
How long is the
garden?
? 10
How wide is the
border?
? 2
You will need 52
tiles and will
have to cover 18
square feet with
topsoil.
This will cost
192 dollars.
```

The problem *More About Borders* poses a variety of questions generalizing the ideas in the original border problem.

If you were running an outdoor supply store, you might often be asked questions like these, and you might not want to figure out the amount of tiling or topsoil needed each time.

Perhaps technology can help. Write a program that answers some or all of the questions posed in *More About Borders.*

At the ultimate level of detail, the program might run something like the display at the left.

As usual, everything but the numbers that follow the question marks is done by the program. The numbers 7, 10, and 2 are entered by the user.

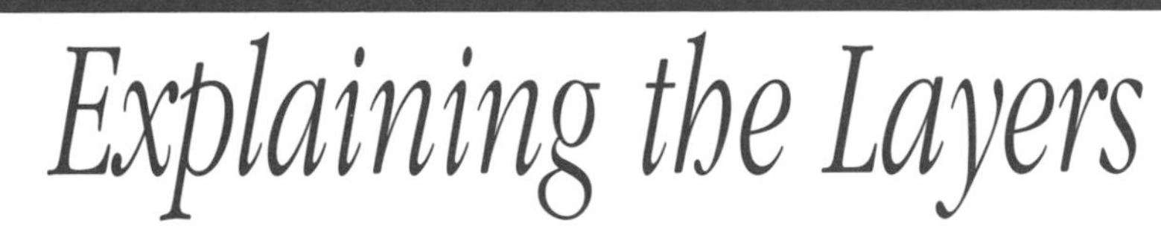

Explaining the Layers

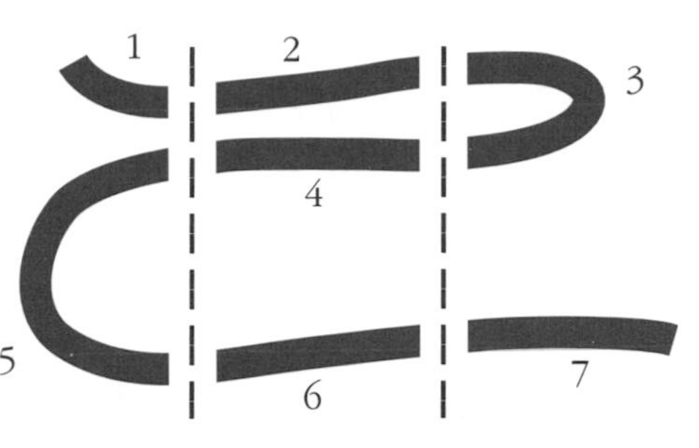

In *Homework 23: Cutting Through the Layers,* you looked at diagrams like the one at the left.

In these diagrams, a single piece of string is bent back and forth into several "layers," and then a number of cuts are made across the bent string. The problem is to figure out how many pieces of string you get.

For example, the diagram above shows three layers of string and two cuts, resulting in seven pieces of string after the cuts.

Your task in that assignment was to find a formula for the number of pieces of string in terms of the number of layers (represented by L) and the number of cuts (represented by C).

Your task in this problem is to write an explanation, in terms of the problem situation, for why your formula works for any number of layers and any number of cuts.

Appendix B Blackline Masters

This appendix contains materials that you will need (or want) for the classroom and that are not in the student book.

- The 46 cards for the *Lonesome Llama* activity on Day 8. Some of these pictures are identical to others, as described in the activity. These pages can be copied onto card stock and cut up so that each house is on a separate card. You will need a complete set of 46 *Lonesome Llama* cards for each group. You will find it easier to keep the sets intact if each complete set of cards is copied onto a different color of card stock.
- A large version of the thermometer diagram used on Day 14. You can make an overhead transparency of this diagram for classroom use.
- The in-class and take-home unit assessments for *Patterns.* You will need to reproduce these for students for Day 25.

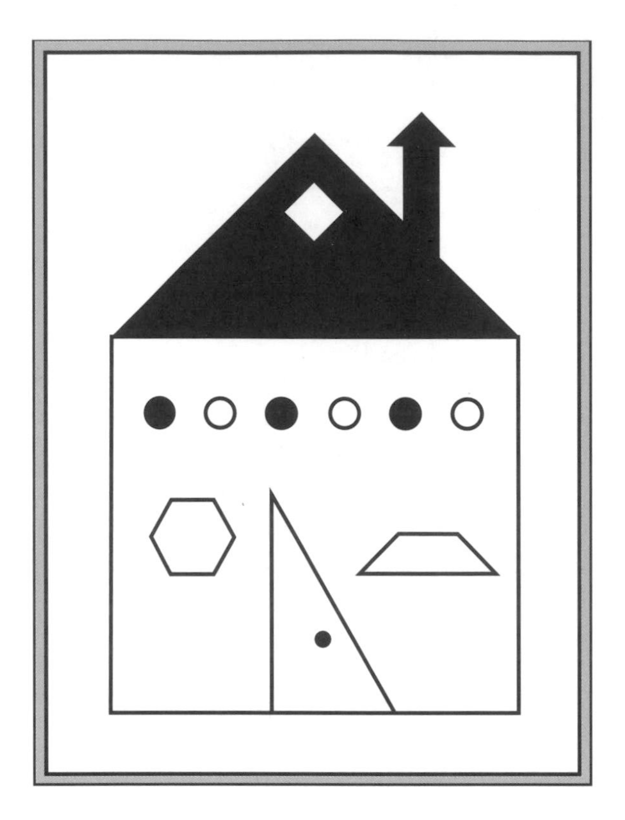
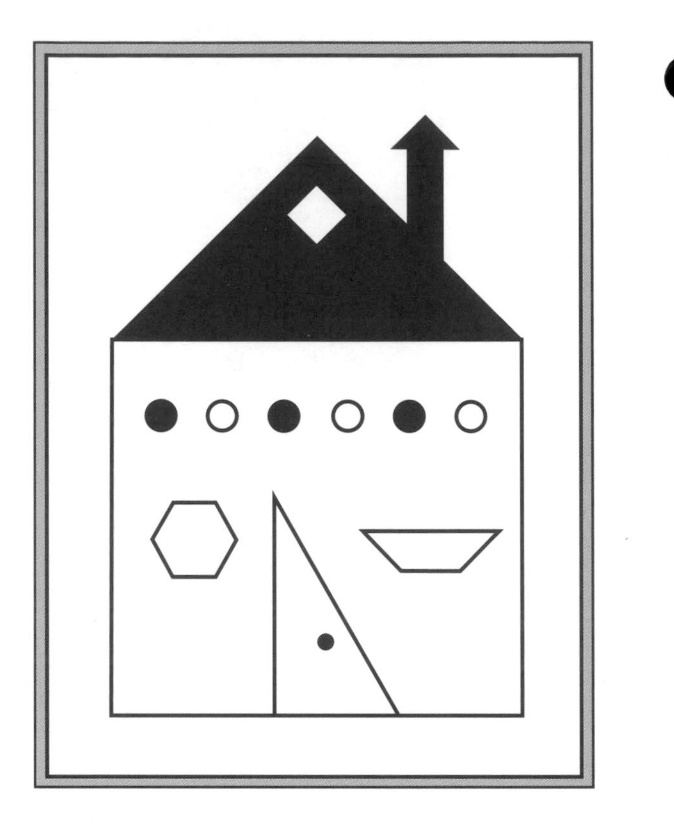

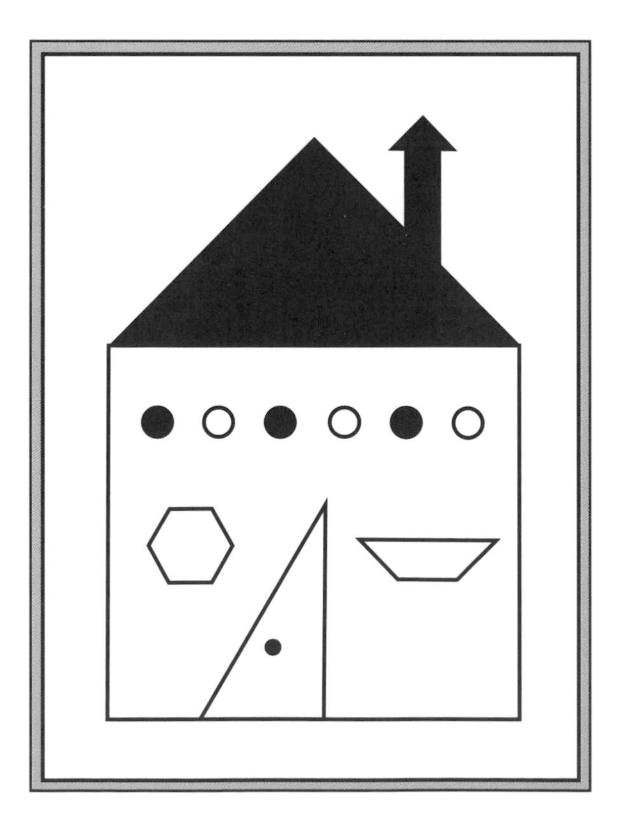

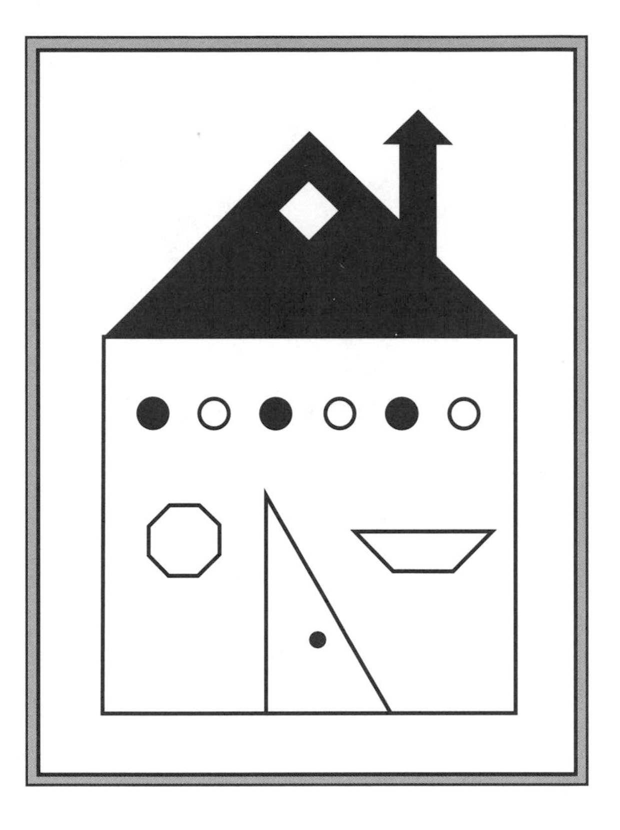
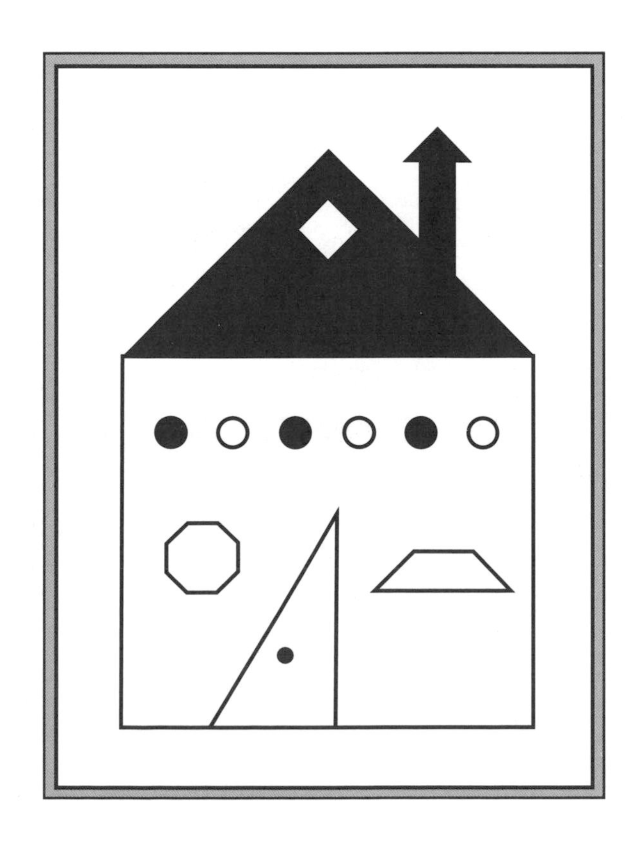

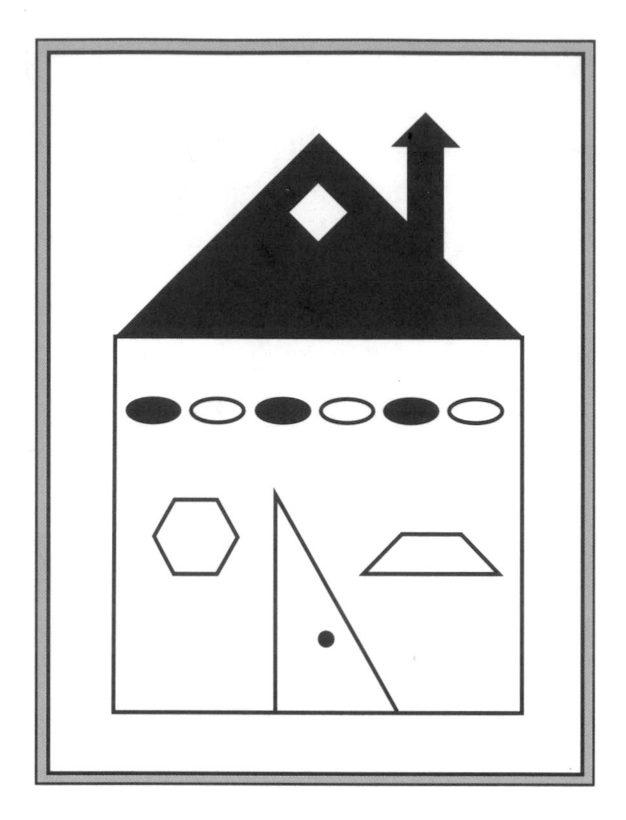

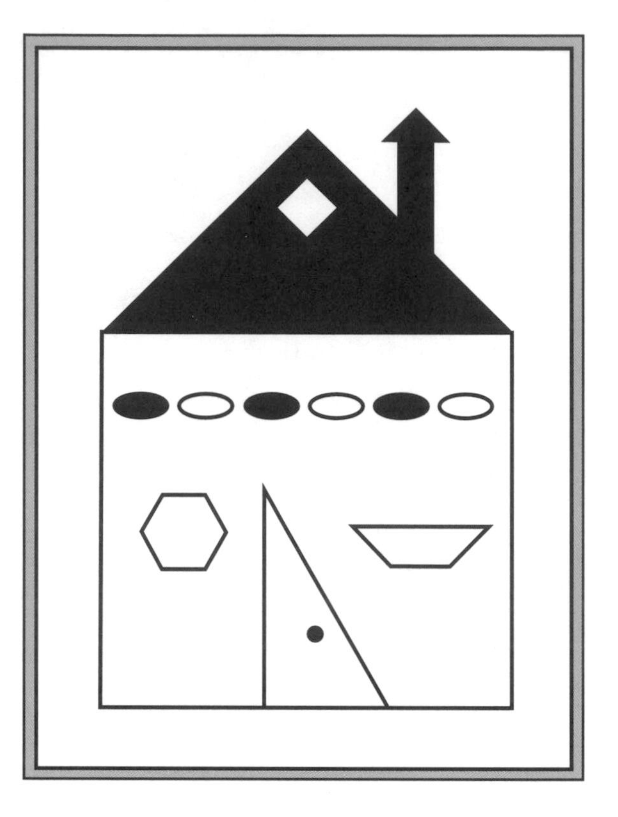

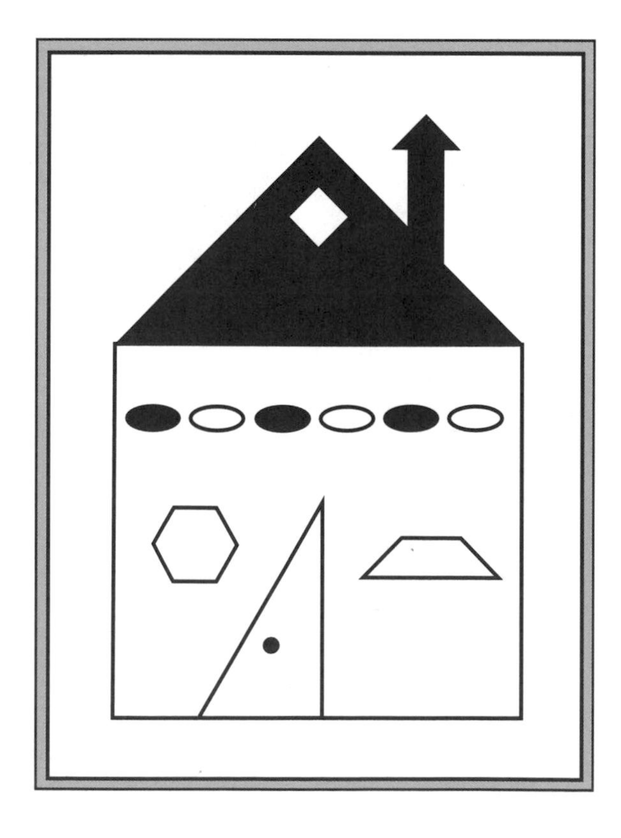

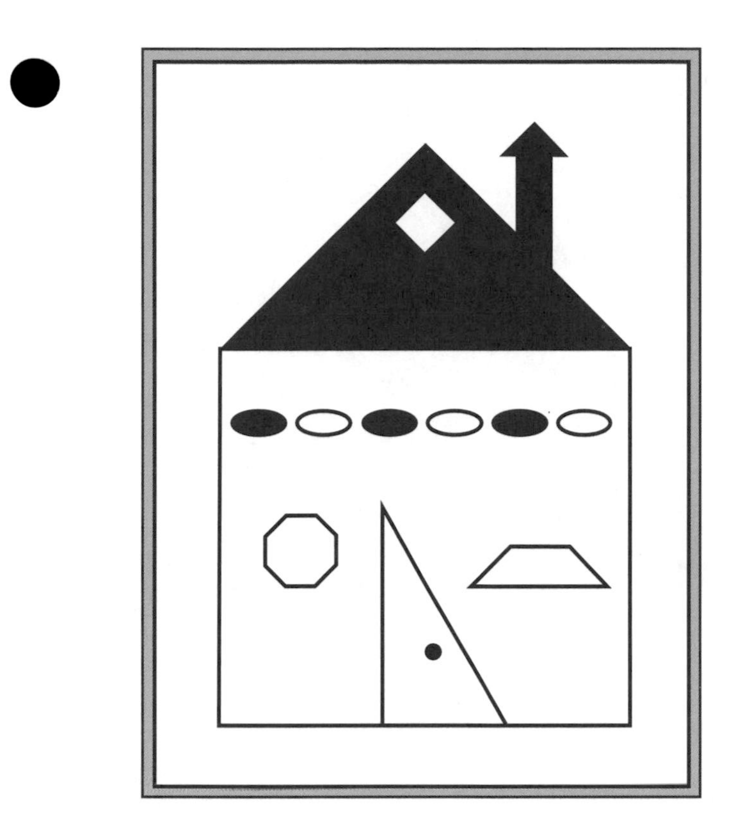
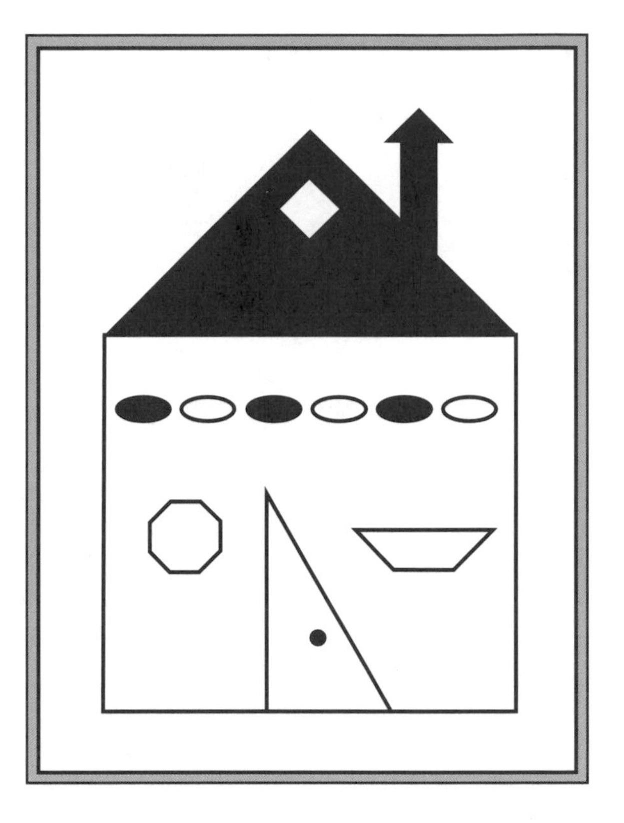
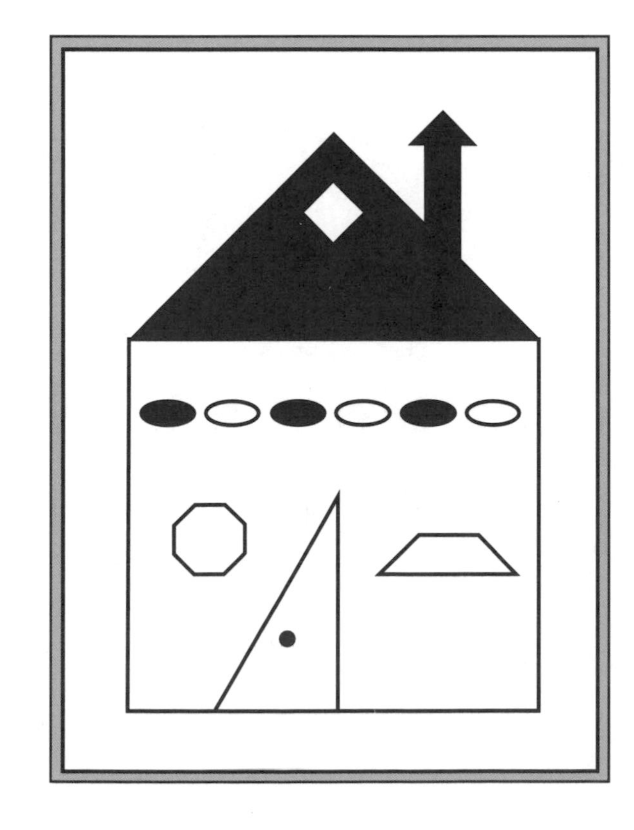

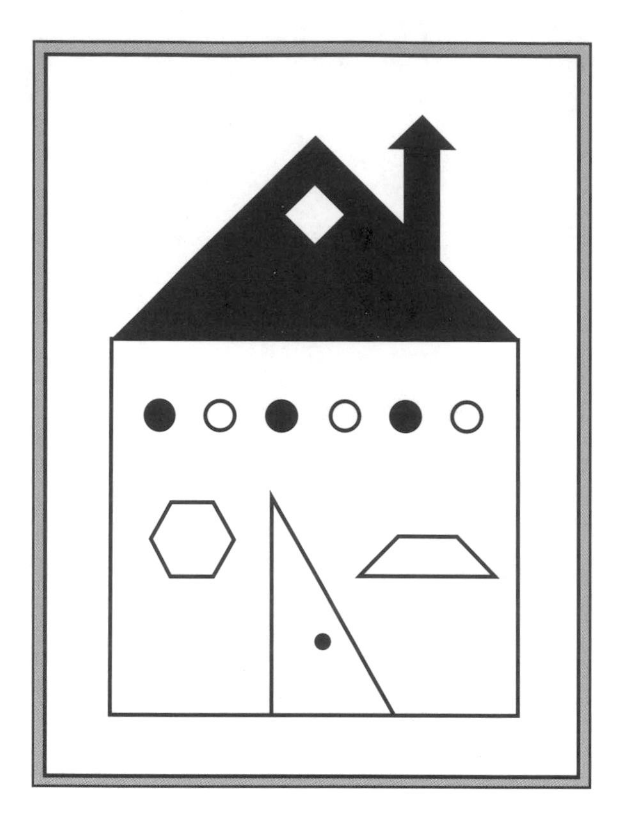

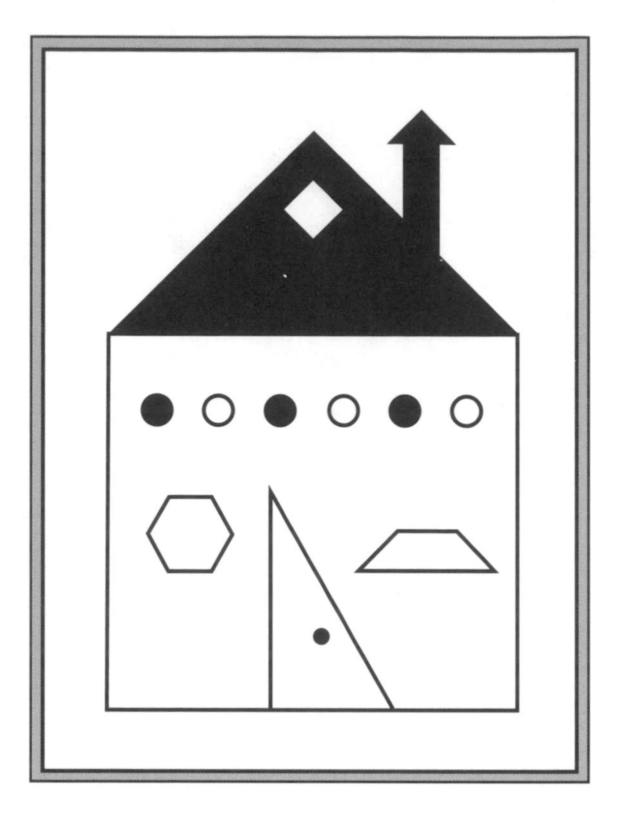

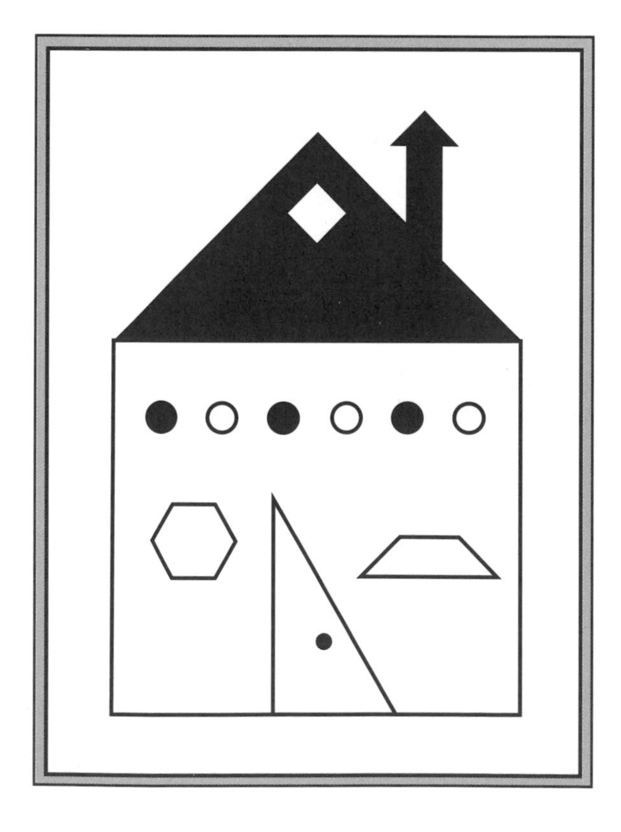

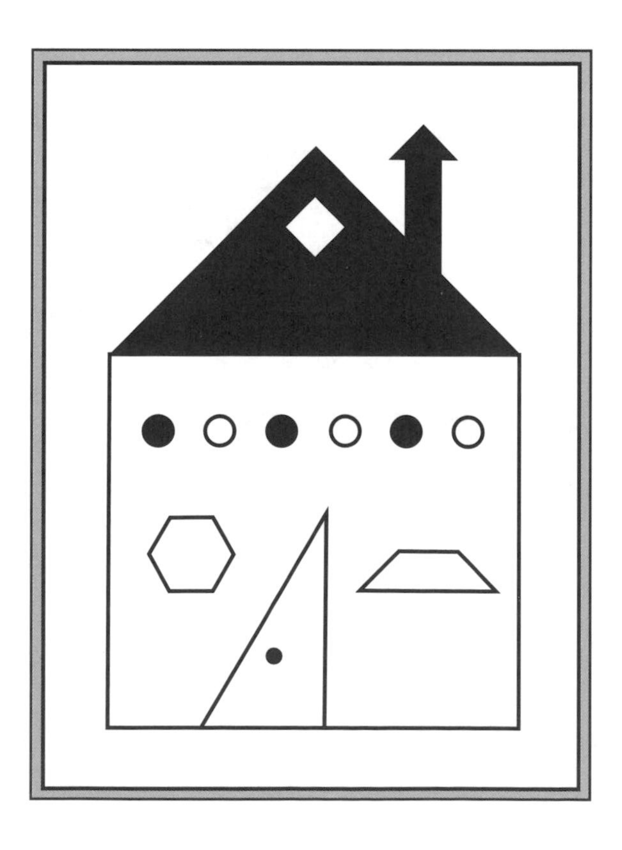

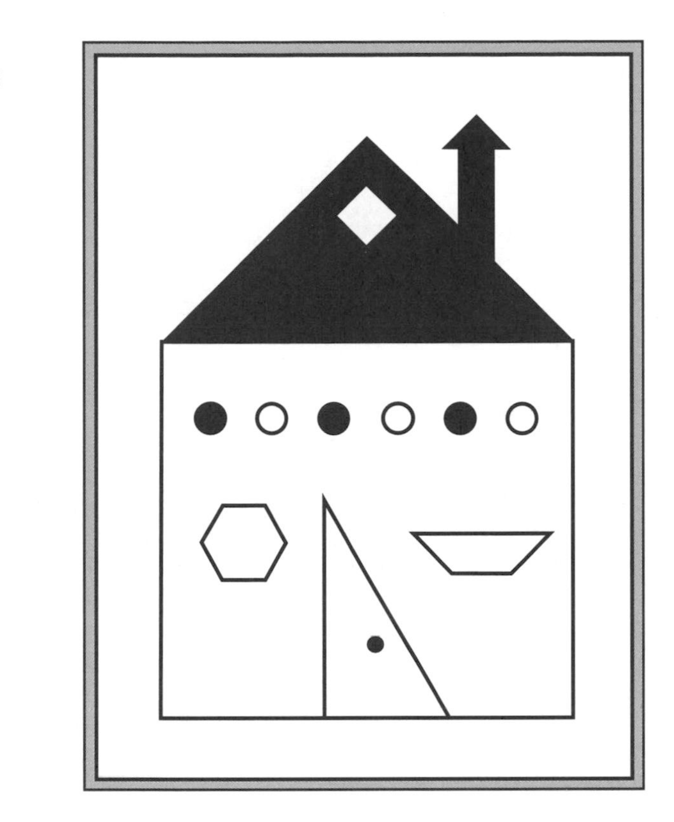

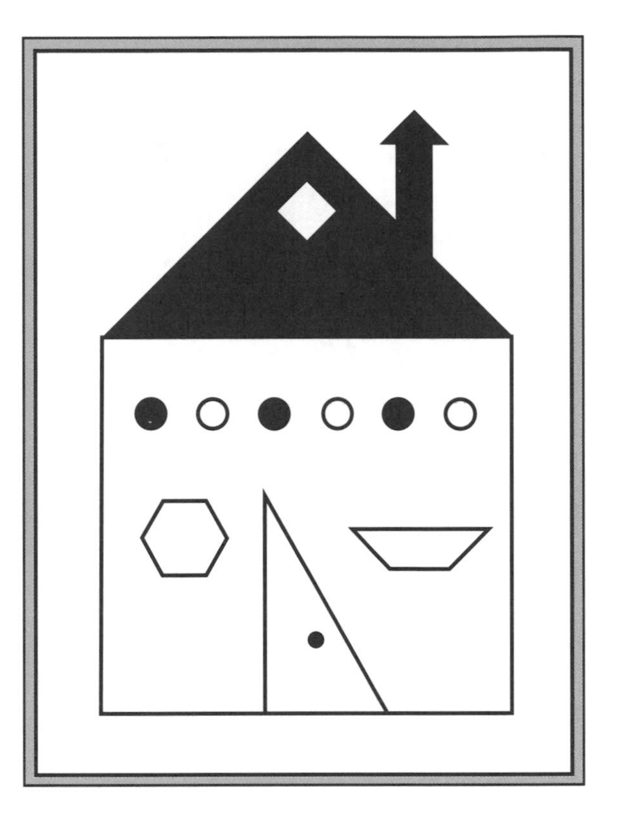

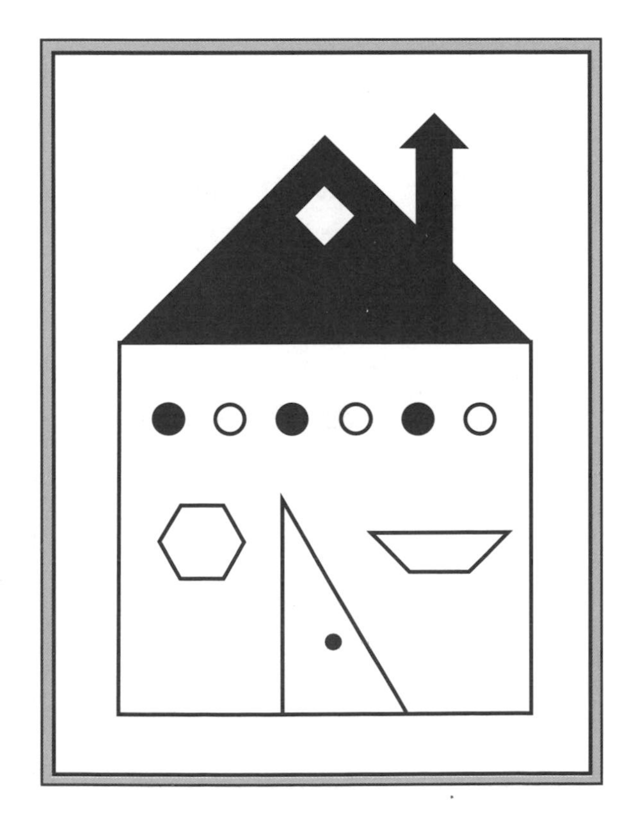

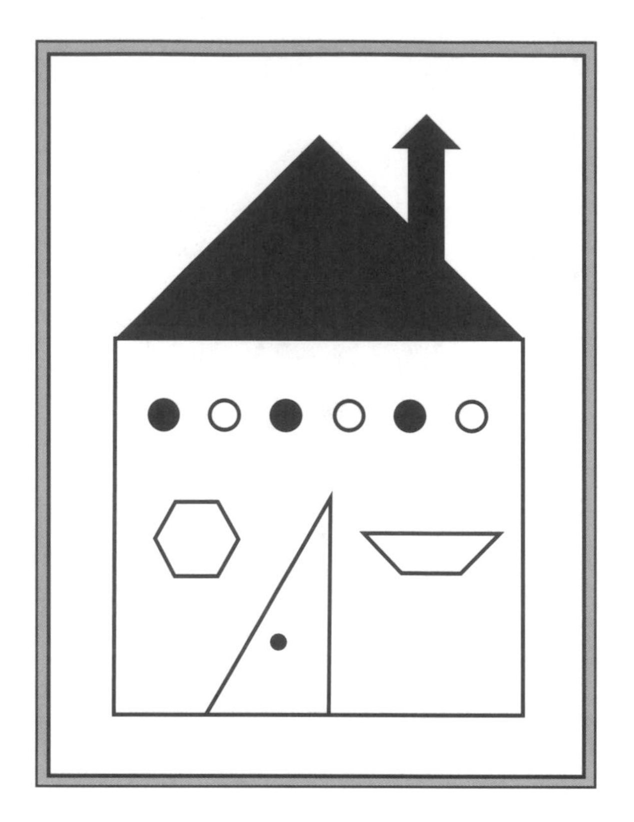
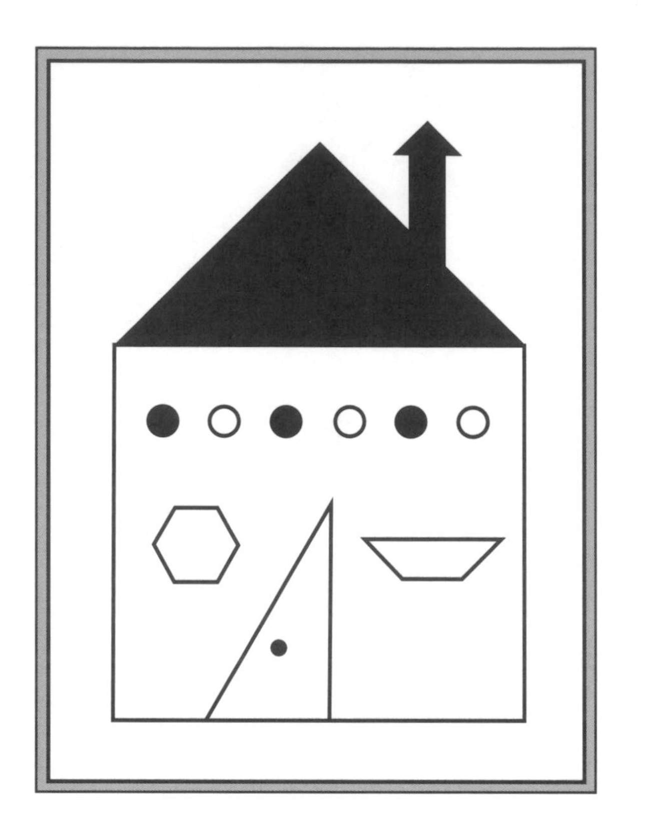
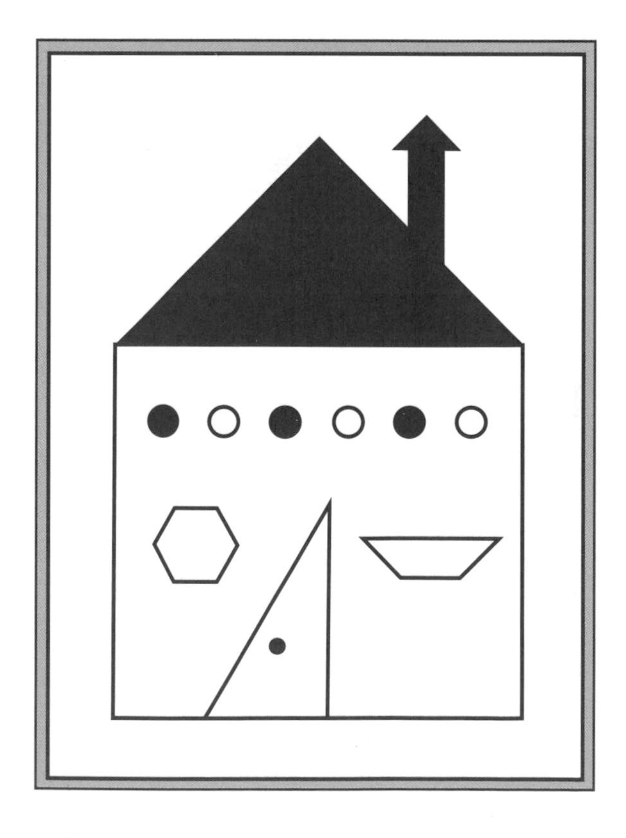
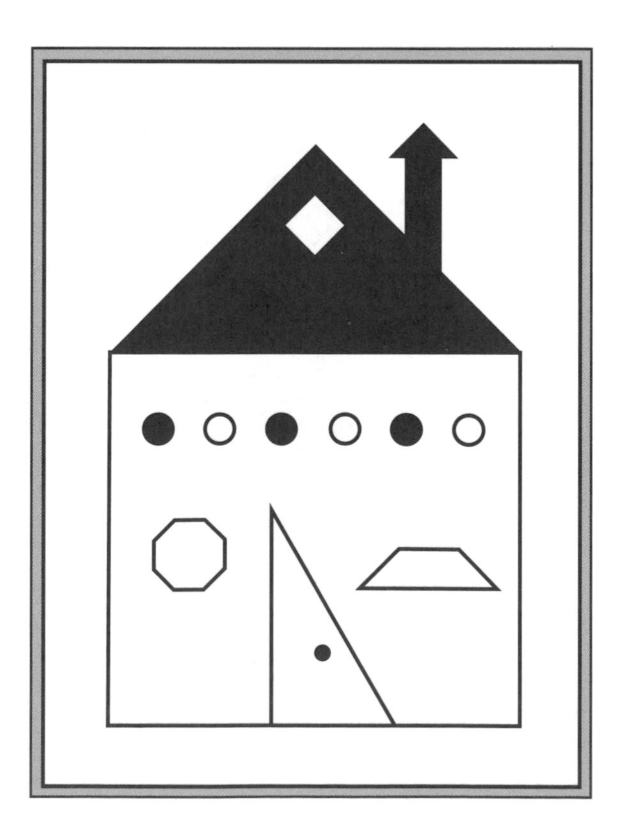

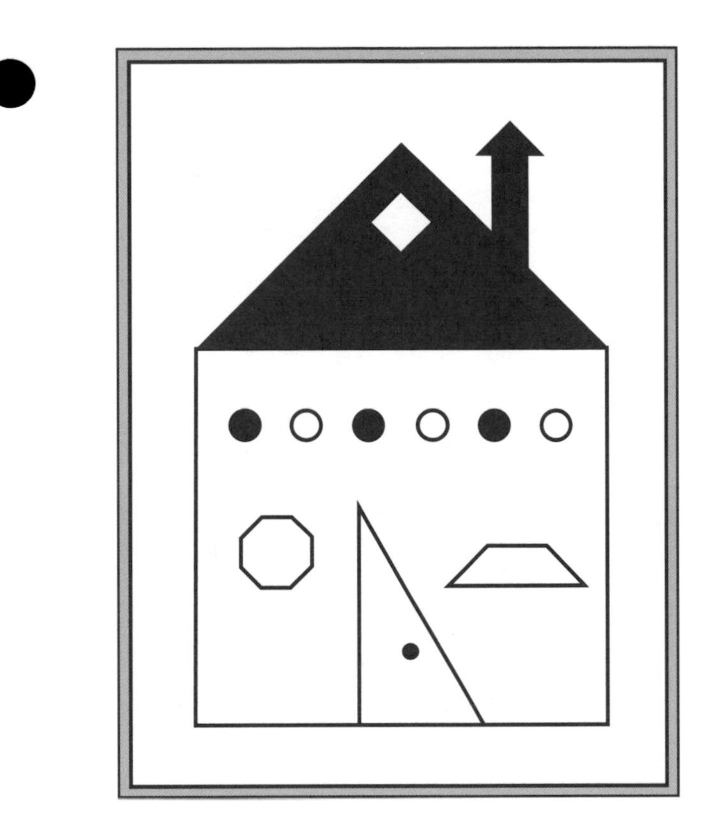
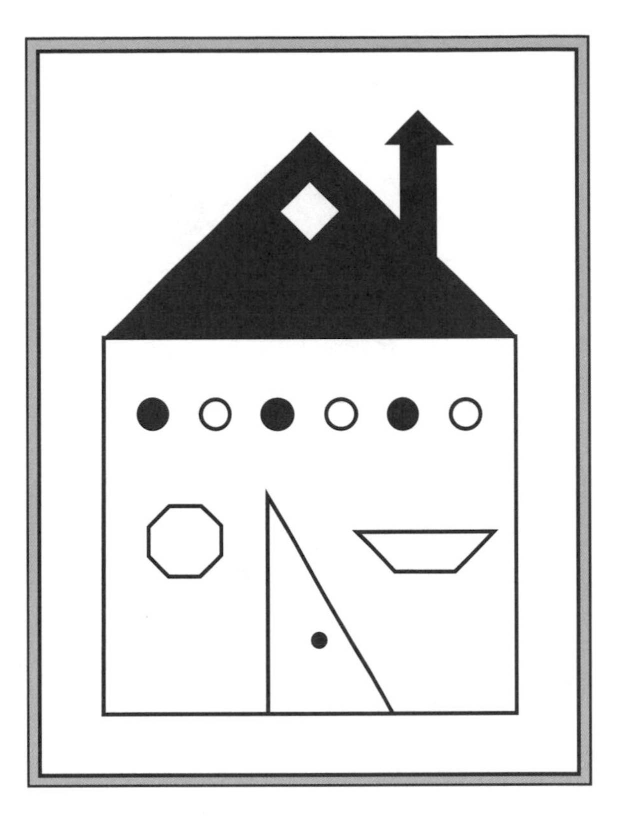
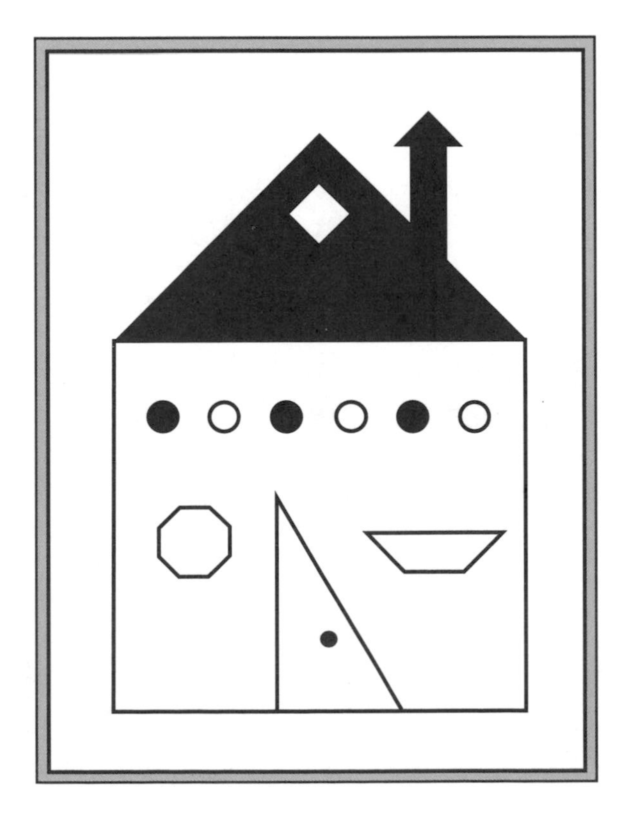
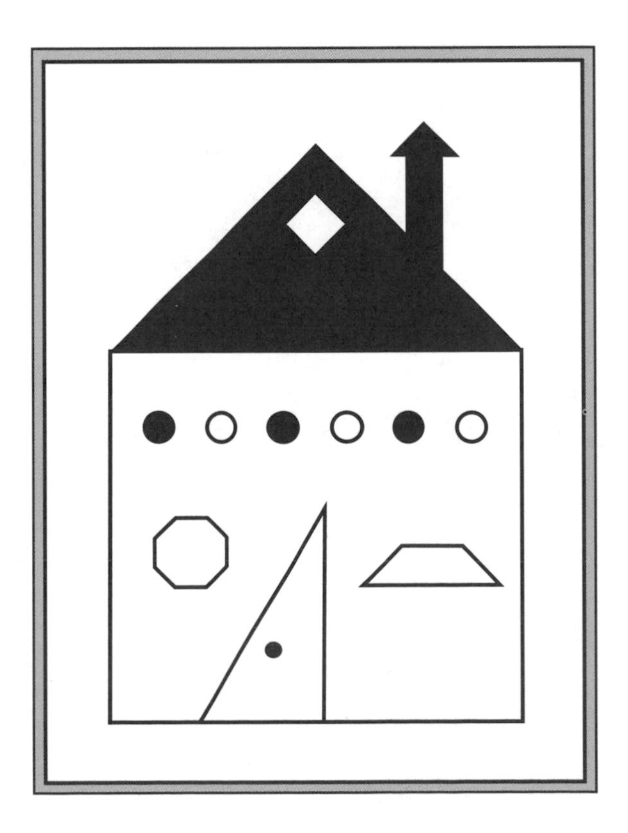

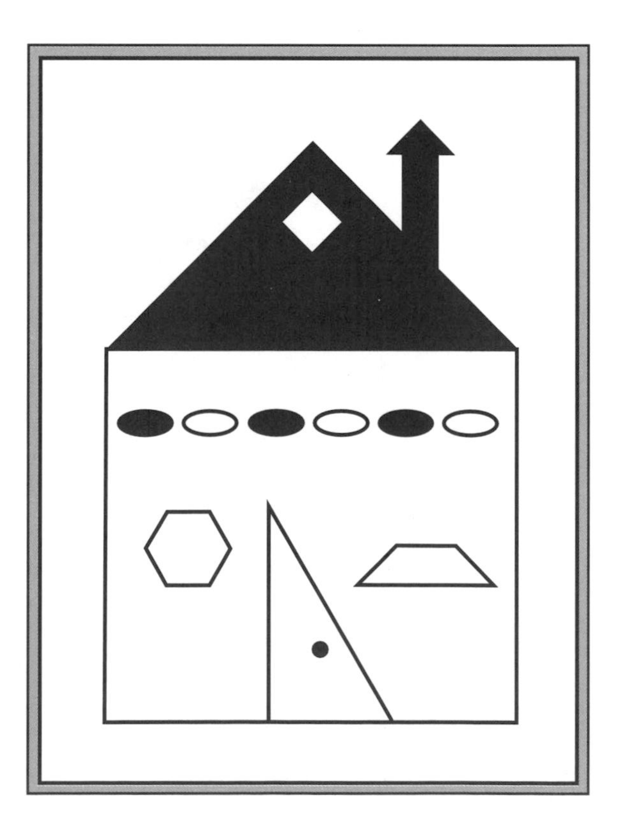

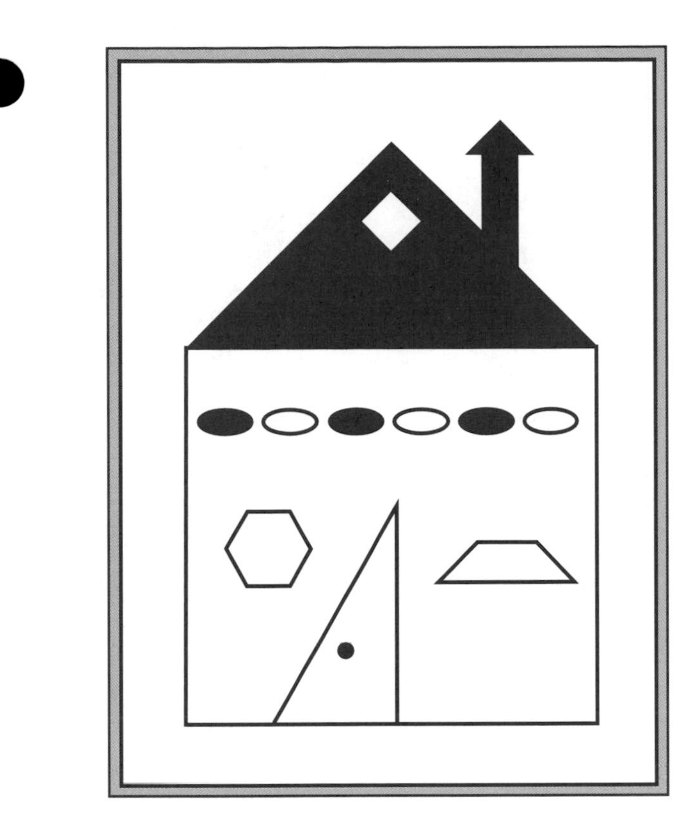
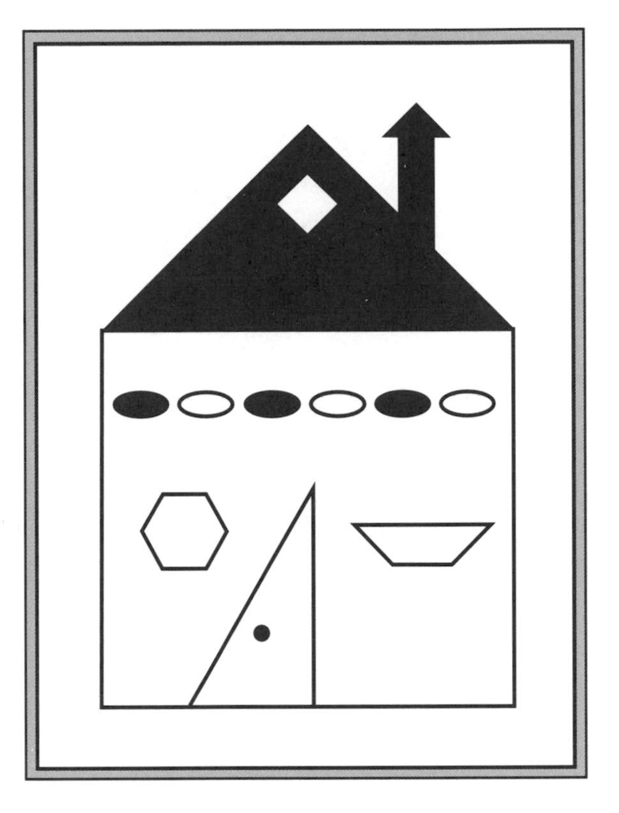
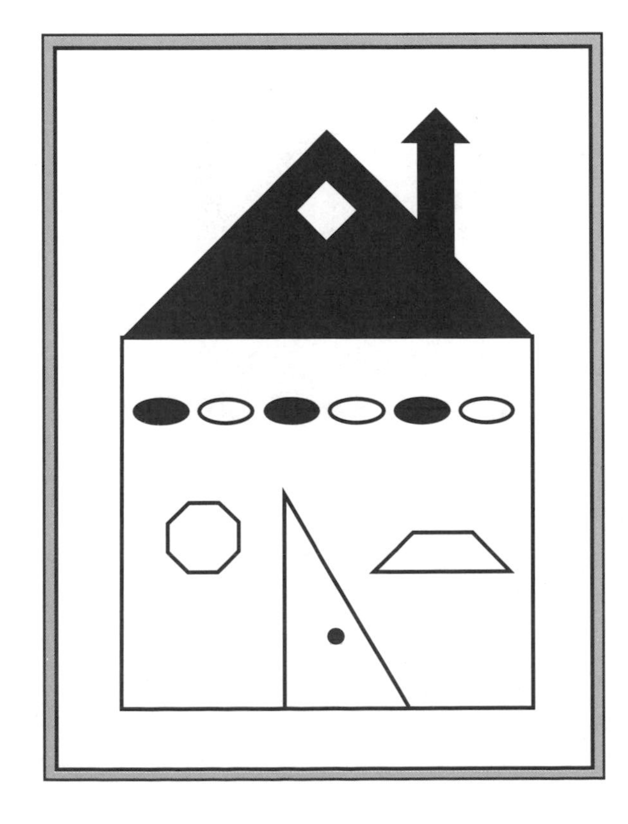
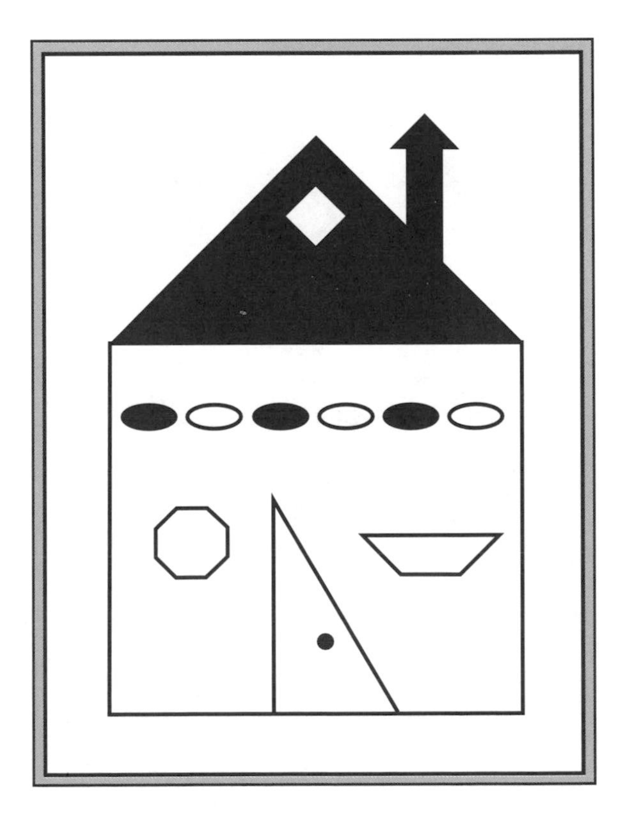

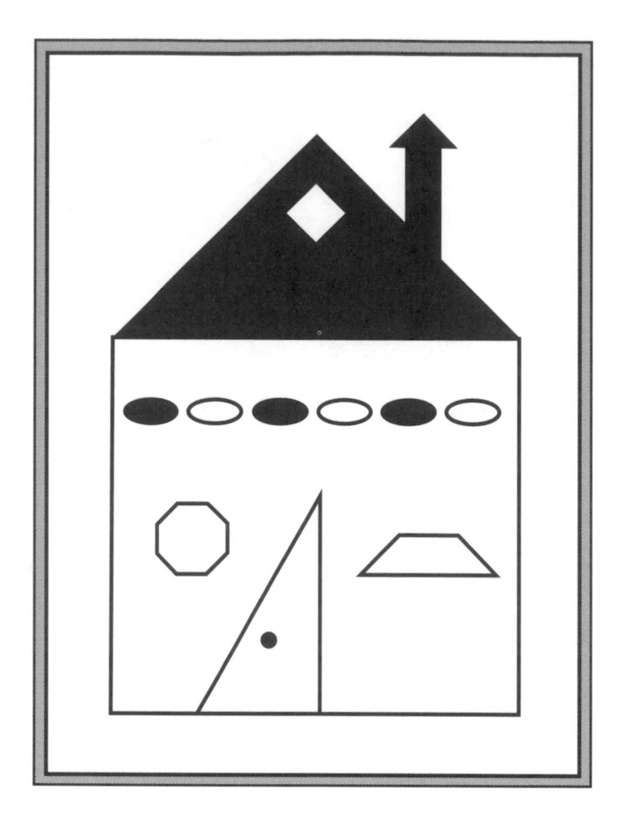

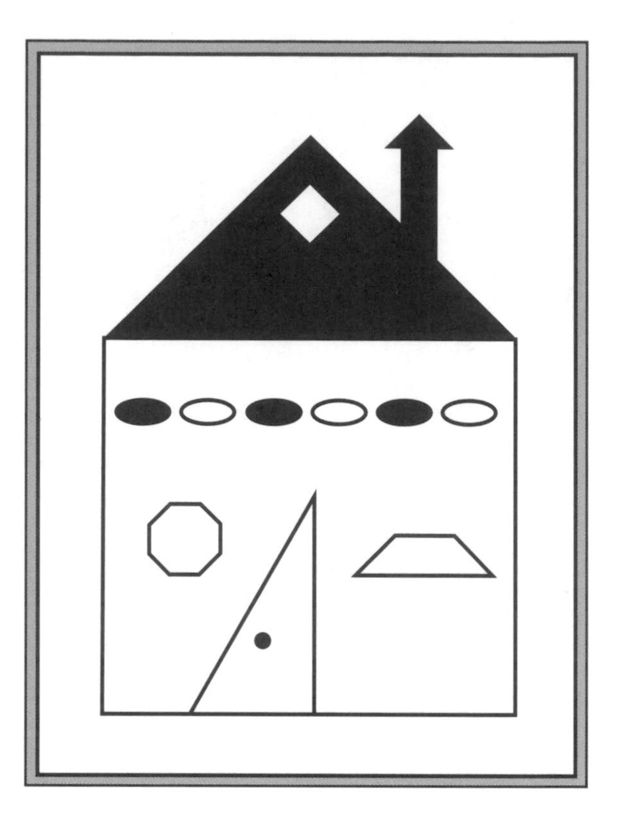

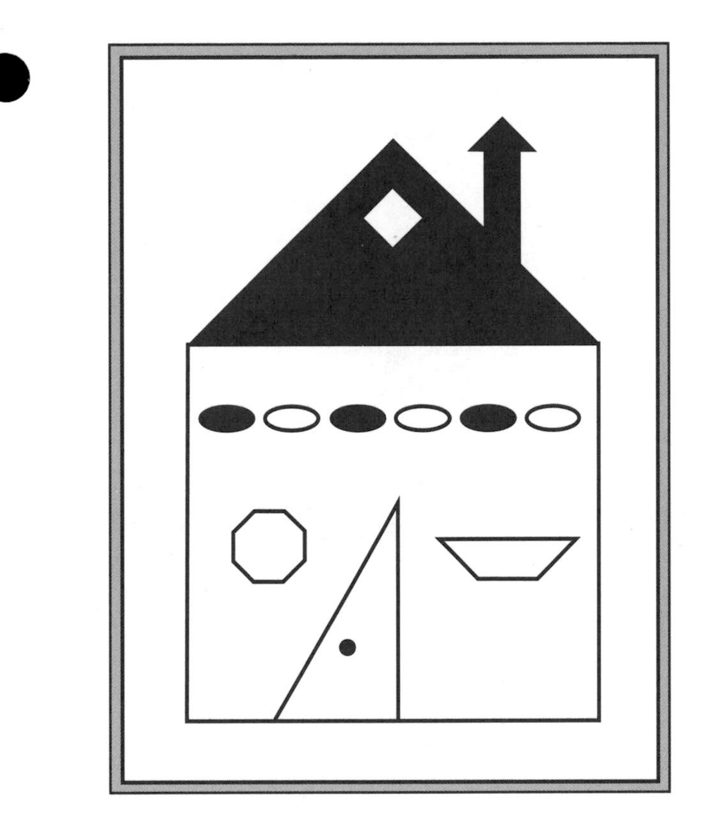

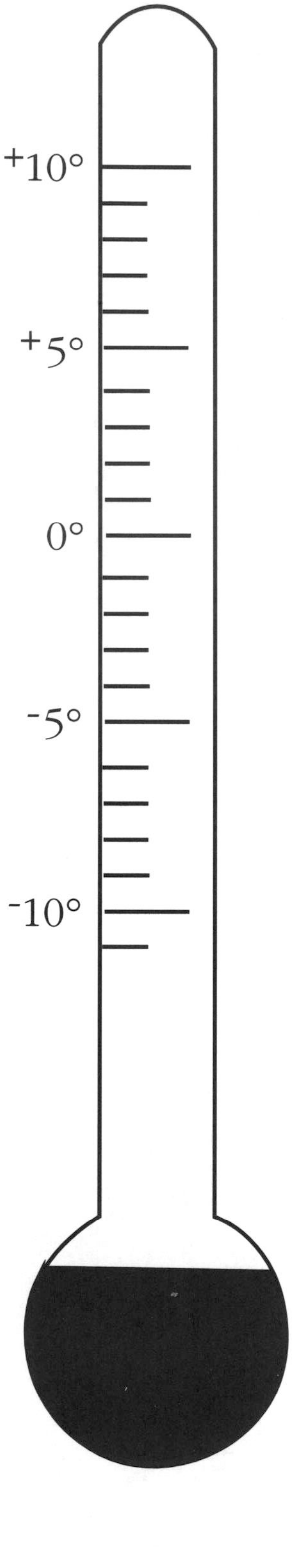

+10°

+5°

0°

-5°

-10°

In-Class Assessment for "Patterns"

1. Explain each of the following problems in terms of the model of hot and cold cubes. Your explanation should include a statement of how the temperature changes overall in each case.

   a. $3 - (-2)$

   b. $5 \cdot (-4)$

In	Out
4	11
8	19
-2	-1
10	?
-5	?
?	31

2. a. Find the missing entries for the In-Out table at the right.

   b. Describe the function shown in the table both in words and by using an algebraic expression.

3. An **isosceles triangle** is a triangle in which at least two of the angles are equal.

   Use the figure at the right to represent a general isosceles triangle in which $\angle B$ and $\angle C$ are equal.

   a. Suppose $\angle B = 70°$. Find the size of $\angle A$.

   b. Suppose $\angle B = 50°$. Find the size of $\angle A$.

   c. Make an In-Out table and develop an expression that will tell you the size of $\angle A$ in terms of the size of $\angle B$. That is, $\angle B$ should be the *In* and $\angle A$ should be the *Out*.

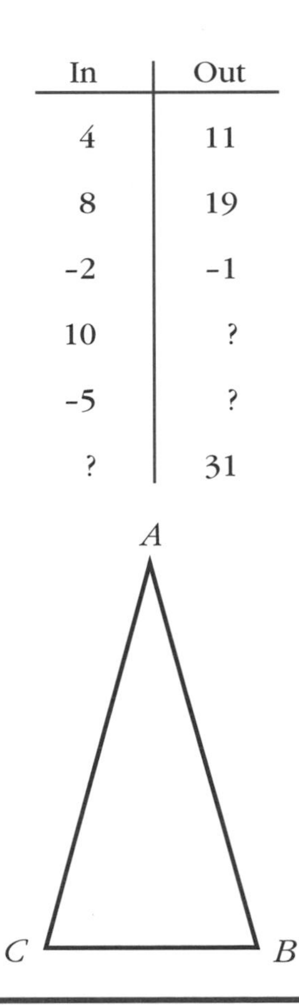

Take-Home Assessment for *Patterns*

This problem is like the border problem, but it involves cubes instead of squares.

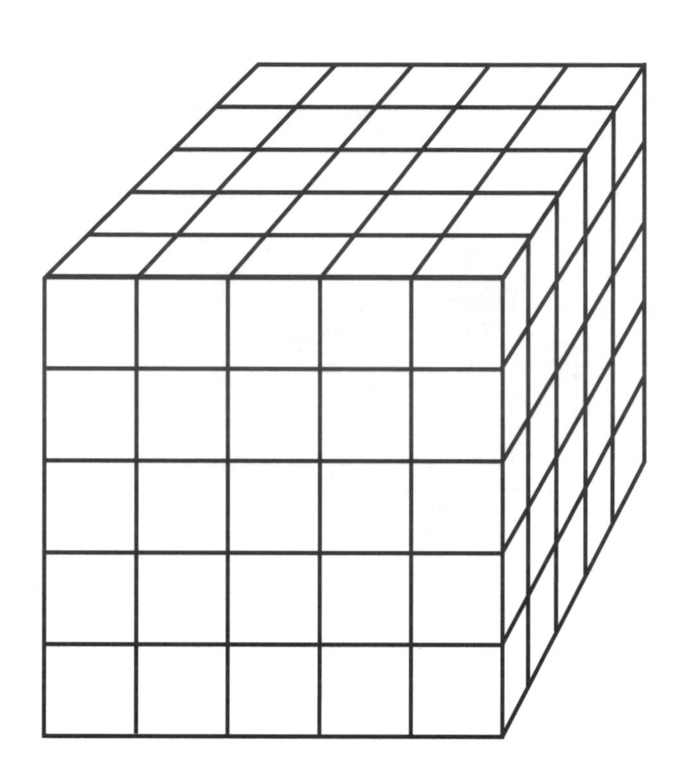

Imagine that you have a cube that is 5 inches long on every side. This large cube is made up of smaller cubes, and each small cube is 1 inch on every side.

Someone comes along and paints the large cube on all of its faces, including the bottom. None of the paint leaks to the inside.

How many of the smaller cubes have any paint at all on them? (Careful! The answer is neither 125 nor 150.)

How many of the smaller cubes have just one face painted?

How many have two faces painted?

Answer the same question for three, four, five, and six faces.

Your write-up for this problem should include

- *Problem Statement:* Restate the problem in your own words.
- *Process:* Please show all the work you did in solving this problem. If you used diagrams or tables, include them.
- *Solution:* Give your solution and justify it so that someone else will be convinced that your solution is correct.

This is the glossary for all five units of IMP Year 1.

Absolute value — The distance a number is from 0 on the number line. The symbol | | stands for absolute value.

Examples: $|-2| = 2$; $|7| = 7$; $|0| = 0$

Acute angle — An angle that measures more than 0° and less than 90°.

Acute triangle — A triangle whose angles are all acute.

Adjacent angles — Two angles with the same vertex and formed using a shared ray.

Example: Angles A and B are adjacent angles.

Adjacent side — (for an acute angle of a right triangle) The side of the right triangle which, together with the hypotenuse, forms the given angle.

Example: In the right triangle ABC, side $\overline{BC}$ is adjacent to $\angle C$, and side $\overline{AB}$ is adjacent to $\angle A$.

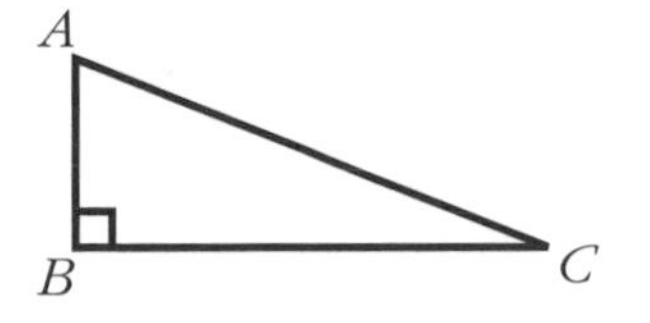

Alternate interior angles — If two lines are intersected by a transversal, then the inside angles that are on opposite sides of the transversal are alternate interior angles.

Example: Angles K and L are one pair of alternate interior angles, and angles M and N are another pair.

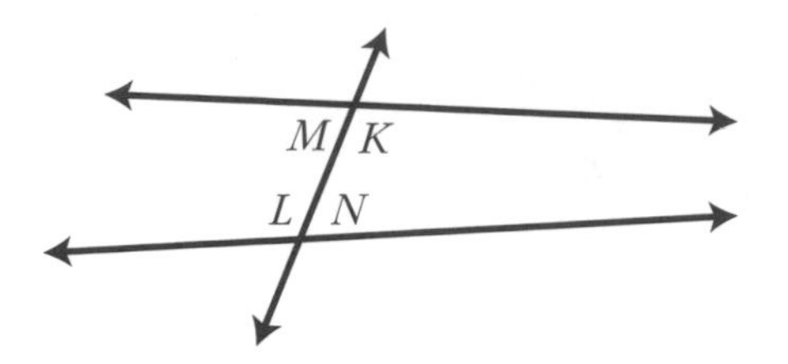

Amplitude
(for a pendulum) The angle of a pendulum's swing, measured from the vertical to the most outward position of the pendulum during its swing.

Example: The pendulum in the diagram has an amplitude of 20°.

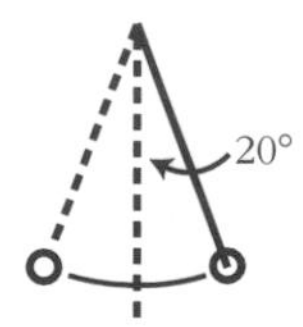

Angle
Informally, an amount of turn, usually measured in **degrees.** Formally, the geometric figure formed by two **rays** with a common initial point, called the **vertex** of the angle.

Angle of elevation
The angle at which an object appears above the horizontal, as measured from a chosen point.

Example: The diagram shows the angle of elevation to the top of the tree from point A.

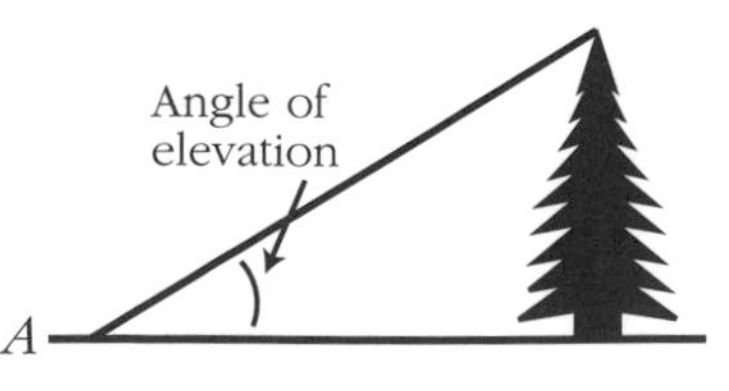

Area
Informally, the amount of space inside a two-dimensional figure, usually measured in square units.

Area model
For probability, a diagram showing the possible outcomes of a particular event. Each portion of the model represents an outcome, and the ratio of the area of that portion to the area of the whole model is the probability of that outcome.

Axis — (plural: **axes**) See **Coordinate system.**

Coefficient — Usually, a number being used to multiply a variable or power of a variable in an algebraic expression.

Example: In the expression $3x + 4x^2$, 3 and 4 are coefficients.

Complementary angles — A pair of angles whose measures add to 90°. If two complementary angles are adjacent, together they form a right angle.

Composite number — A counting number having more than two whole-number divisors.

Example: 12 is a composite number because it has the divisors 1, 2, 3, 4, 6, and 12.

Conclusion — Informally, any statement arrived at by reasoning or through examples.

See also **"If . . . , then . . ." statement.**

Conditional probability — The probability that an event will occur based on the assumption that some other event has already occurred.

Congruent — Informally, having the same shape and size. Formally, two polygons are congruent if their corresponding angles have equal measure and their corresponding sides are equal in length. The symbol ≅ means "is congruent to."

Conjecture — A theory or an idea about how something works, usually based on examples.

Constraint — Informally, a limitation or restriction.

Continuous graph — Informally, a graph that can be drawn without lifting the pencil, in contrast to a **discrete graph.**

Coordinate system — A way to represent points in the plane with pairs of numbers called **coordinates**. The system is based on two perpendicular lines, one horizontal and one vertical, called **coordinate axes.** The point where the lines meet is called the **origin.** Traditionally, the axes are labeled with the variables x and y as shown below. The horizontal axis is often called the **x-axis** and the vertical axis is often called the **y-axis.**

Example: Point A has coordinates (3, -2).

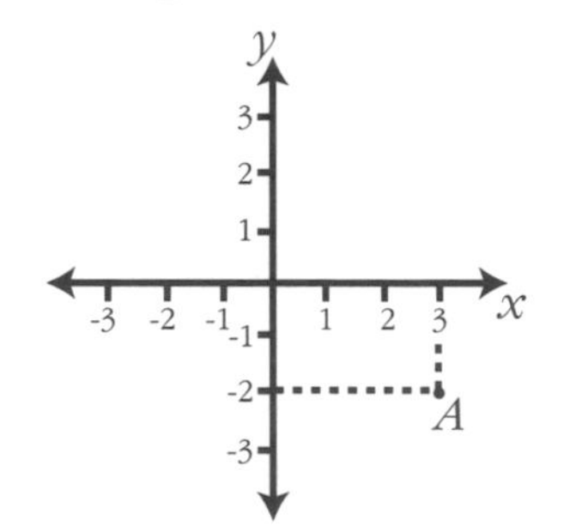

Corresponding angles (for a transversal) If two lines are intersected by a transversal, then two angles are corresponding angles if they occupy the same position relative to the transversal and the other lines that form them.

Example: Angles A and D are a pair of corresponding angles, and angles B and E are another pair of corresponding angles.

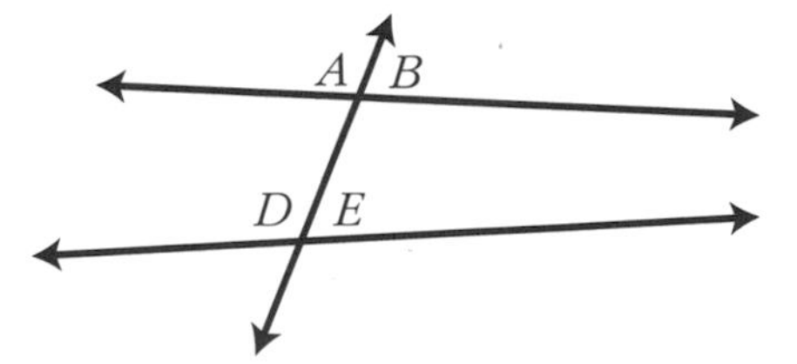

Corresponding parts For a pair of similar or congruent polygons, sides or angles of the two polygons that have the same relative position.

Example: Side a in the small triangle and side b in the large triangle are corresponding parts.

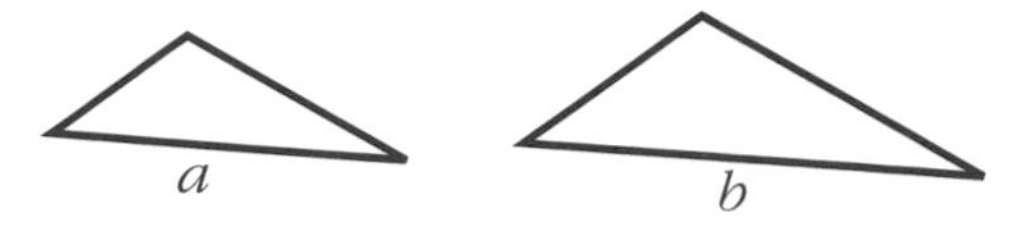

Counterexample An example which demonstrates that a conjecture is not true.

Degree The measurement unit for an angle defined by having a complete turn equal to 360 degrees. The symbol ° represents degrees.

Diagonal In a polygon, a line segment that connects two vertices and that is not a side of the polygon.

Discrete graph A graph consisting of isolated or unconnected points, in contrast to a **continuous graph.**

Divisor A factor of an integer.

Example: 1, 2, 3, 4, 6, and 12 are the positive divisors of 12.

Domain The set of values that can be used as inputs for a given function.

Equilateral triangle A triangle with all sides the same length.

Expected value In a game or other probability situation, the average amount gained or lost per turn in the long run.

Exterior angle An angle formed outside a polygon by extending one of its sides.

Example: The diagram shows an exterior angle for polygon *ABCDE*.

Factor The same as **divisor.**

Factorial The product of all the whole numbers from a particular number down to 1. The symbol ! stands for factorial.

Example: 5! (read "five factorial") means $5 \cdot 4 \cdot 3 \cdot 2 \cdot 1$.

Fair game A game in which both players are expected to come out equally well in the long run.

Frequency bar graph

A bar graph showing how often each result occurs.

Example: This frequency bar graph shows, for instance, that 11 times in 80 rolls, the sum of two dice was 6.

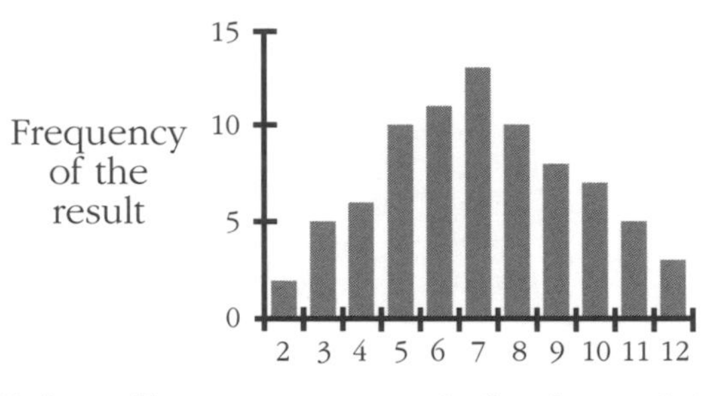

Function

Informally, a process or rule for determining the numerical value of one variable in terms of another. A function is often represented as a set of number pairs in which the second number is determined by the first, according to the function rule.

Graph

A mathematical diagram for displaying information.

Hexagon

A polygon with six sides.

Hypotenuse

The longest side in a right triangle, or the length of this side. The hypotenuse is located opposite the right angle.

Example: In right triangle *ABC*, the hypotenuse is $\overline{AC}$.

Hypothesis

Informally, a theory about a situation or about how a certain set of data is behaving. Also, a set of assumptions being used to analyze or understand a situation.

See also **"If . . . , then . . ." statement.**

"If . . . , then . . ." statement

A specific form of mathematical statement, saying that if one condition is true, then another condition must also be true.

Example: Here is a true "If . . . , then . . ." statement.

If two angles of a triangle have equal measure, then the sides opposite these angles have equal length.

The condition "two angles of a triangle have equal measure" is the **hypothesis.** The condition "the sides opposite these angles have equal length" is the **conclusion.**

Independent events — Two (or more) events are independent if the outcome of one does not influence the outcome of the other.

Integer — Any number that is either a counting number, zero, or the opposite of a counting number. The integers can be represented using set notation as

$$\{\ldots -3, -2, -1, 0, 1, 2, 3, \ldots\}.$$

Examples: -4, 0, and 10 are integers.

Interior angle — An angle inside a figure, especially within a polygon.

Example: Angle BAE is an interior angle of the polygon $ABCDE$.

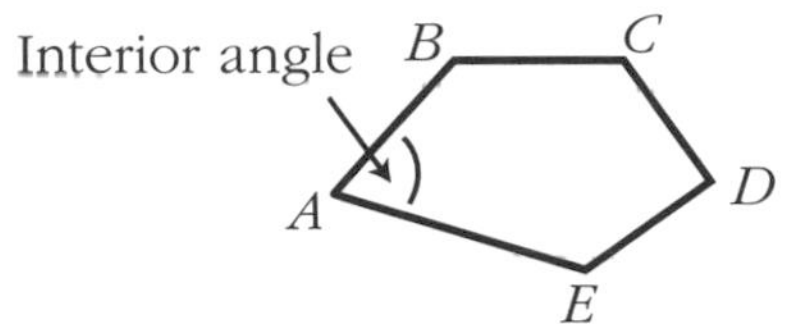

Isosceles triangle — A triangle with two sides of equal length.

Leg — Either of the two shorter sides in a right triangle. The two legs of a right triangle form the right angle of the triangle. The longest side of a right triangle (the hypotenuse) is not considered a leg.

Line of best fit — Informally, the line that comes closest to fitting a given set of points on a discrete graph.

Line segment — The portion of a straight line between two given points.

Mathematical model — A mathematical description or structure used to represent how a real-life situation works.

Mean — The numerical average of a data set, found by adding the data items and dividing by the number of items in the set.

Example: For the data set 8, 12, 12, 13, and 17, the sum of the data items is 62 and there are 5 items in the data set, so the mean is 62 ÷ 5, or 12.4.

Measurement variation The situation of taking several measurements of the same thing and getting different results.

Median (of a set of data) The "middle number" in a set of data that has been arranged from smallest to largest.

Example: For the data set 4, 17, 22, 56, and 100, the median is 22, because it is the number in the middle of the list.

Mode (of a set of data) The number that occurs most often in a set of data. Many sets of data do not have a single mode.

Example: For the data set 3, 4, 7, 16, 18, 18, and 23, the mode is 18.

Natural number Any of the counting numbers 1, 2, 3, 4, and so on.

Normal distribution A certain precisely defined set of probabilities, which can often be used to approximate real-life events. Sometimes used to refer to any data set whose frequency bar graph is approximately "bell-shaped."

Observed probability The likelihood of a certain event happening based on observed results, as distinct from **theoretical probability.**

Obtuse angle An angle that measures more than 90° and less than 180°.

Obtuse triangle A triangle with an obtuse angle.

Octagon An eight-sided polygon.

Opposite side The side of a triangle across from a given angle.

Order of operations A set of conventions that mathematicians have agreed to use whenever a calculation involves more than one operation.

Example: $2 + 3 \cdot 4$ is 14, not 20, because the conventions for order of operations tell us to multiply before we add.

Ordered pair	Two numbers paired together using the format (x, y), often used to locate a point in the coordinate system.
Origin	See **Coordinate system.**
Parallel lines	Two lines in a plane that do not intersect.
Pentagon	A five-sided polygon.
Perimeter	The boundary of a polygon, or the total length of this boundary.
Period	The length of time for a cyclical event to complete one full cycle.
Perpendicular lines	A pair of lines that form a right angle.
Polygon	A closed two-dimensional shape formed by three or more line segments. The line segments that form a polygon are called its sides. The endpoints of these segments are called **vertices** (singular: **vertex**). Examples: All the figures below are polygons.
Prime number	A whole number greater than 1 that has only two whole number divisors, 1 and itself. Example: 7 is a prime number, because its only whole number divisors are 1 and 7.
Probability	The likelihood of a certain event happening. For a situation involving equally likely outcomes, the probability that the outcome of an event will be an outcome within a given set is defined by a ratio:

$$\text{Probability} = \frac{\text{number of outcomes in the set}}{\text{total number of possible outcomes}}$$

Example: If a die has 2 red faces and 4 green faces, the probability of getting a green face is

$$\frac{\text{number of green faces}}{\text{total number of faces}} = \frac{4}{6}$$

Proof — An absolutely convincing argument.

Proportion — A statement that two ratios are equal.

Proportional — Having the same ratio.

Example: Corresponding sides of triangles *ABC* and *DEF* are proportional, because the ratios $\frac{4}{6}$, $\frac{8}{12}$, and $\frac{10}{15}$ are equal.

Quadrant — One of the four areas created in a coordinate system by using the x-axis and the y-axis as boundaries. The quadrants have standard numbering as shown below.

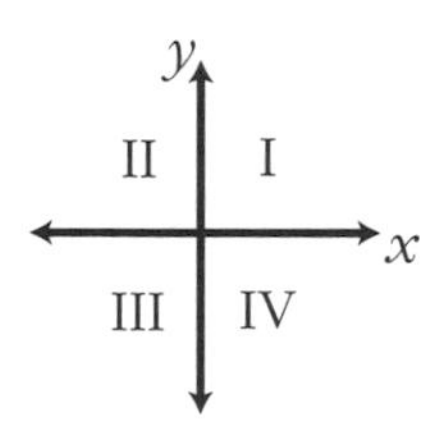

Quadrilateral — A four-sided polygon.

Random — Used in probability to indicate that any of several events is equally likely or that an event is selected from a set of events according to a precisely described distribution.

Range — (of a set of data) The difference between the largest and smallest numbers in the set.

Example: For the data set 7, 12, 18, 18, and 29, the range is 29 - 7, or 22.

Ray — The part of a line from a single point, called the **vertex,** through another point on the line and continuing infinitely in that direction.

Rectangle — A four-sided polygon whose angles are all right angles.

Regular polygon — A polygon whose sides all have equal length and whose angles all have equal measure.

Rhombus — A four-sided polygon whose sides all have the same length.

Right angle — An angle that measures 90°.

Right triangle — A triangle with a right angle.

Sample standard deviation — The calculation on a set of data taken from a larger population of data, used to estimate the standard deviation of the larger population.

Sequence — A list of numbers or expressions, usually following a pattern or rule.

Example: 1, 3, 5, 7, 9, . . . is the sequence of positive odd numbers.

Similar — Informally, having the same shape. Formally, two polygons are similar if their corresponding angles have equal measure and their corresponding sides are proportional in length. The symbol ~ means "is similar to."

Simulation — An experiment or set of experiments using a model of a certain event that is based on the same probabilities as the real event. Simulations allow people to estimate the likelihood of an event when it is impractical to experiment with the real event.

Slope — Informally, the steepness of a line.

Solution — A number that, when substituted for a variable in an equation, makes the equation a true statement.

Example: The value $x = 3$ is a solution to the equation $2x = 6$ because $2 \cdot 3 = 6$.

Square — A four-sided polygon with all sides of equal length and with four right angles.

Square root A number whose square is a given number. The symbol $\sqrt{\ }$ is used to denote the nonnegative square root of a number.

Example: Both 6 and -6 are square roots of 36, because $6^2 = 36$ and $(-6)^2 = 36$; $\sqrt{36} = 6$.

Standard deviation A specific measurement of how spread out a set of data is, usually represented by the lowercase Greek letter sigma (σ).

Straight angle An angle that measures 180°. The rays forming a straight angle together make up a straight line.

Strategy A complete plan about how to proceed in a game or problem situation. A strategy for a game should tell a person exactly what to do under any situation that can arise in the game.

Supplementary angles A pair of angles whose measures add to 180°. If two supplementary angles are adjacent, together they form a straight angle.

Term (of an algebraic expression) A part of an algebraic expression, combined with other terms using addition or subtraction.

Example: The expression $2x^2 + 3x - 12$ has three terms: $2x^2$, $3x$, and 12.

Term (of a sequence) One of the items listed in a sequence.

Example: In the sequence 3, 5, 7, . . . , the number 3 is the first term, 5 is the second term, and so on.

Theoretical probability The likelihood of an event occurring, as explained by a theory or model, as distinct from **observed probability.**

Transversal A line that intersects two or more other lines.

Example: The line l is a transversal that intersects the lines m and n.

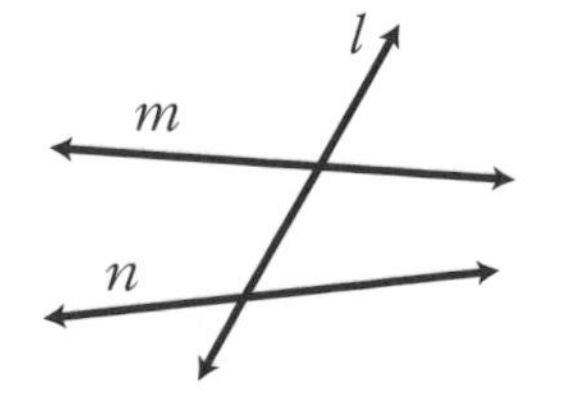

Trapezoid A four-sided polygon with exactly one pair of parallel sides.

Example: Quadrilateral $PQRS$ is a trapezoid, because $\overline{QR}$ and $\overline{PS}$ are parallel and $\overline{PQ}$ and $\overline{SR}$ are not parallel.

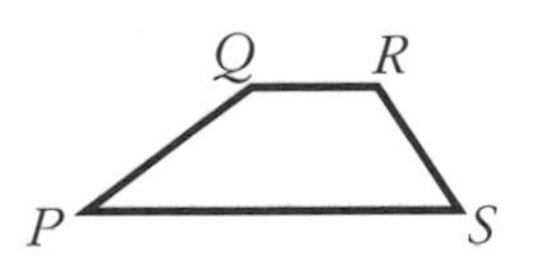

Triangle A polygon with three sides.

Triangle inequality principle The principle that the lengths of any two sides of a triangle must add up to more than the length of the third side.

Trigonometric function Any of six functions defined for acute angles in terms of ratios of sides of a right triangle.

Vertex (plural: **vertices**) See **Angle, Polygon,** and **Ray.**

Vertical angles A pair of "opposite" angles formed by a pair of intersecting lines.

Example: Angles F and G are vertical angles.

Whole number A number that is either zero or a counting number.

x-intercept A place on a graph where a line or curve crosses the x-axis.

y-intercept A place on a graph where a line or curve crosses the y-axis.

Photographic Credits

Teacher Book Classroom Photography

17 Marshall High School, Maureen Burkhart; **37** Lincoln High School, Lori Green; **60** Capuchino High School, Chicha Lynch; **67** Lincoln High School, Lori Green; **91** Lincoln High School, Lori Green; **125** Lincoln High School, Lori Green; **151** San Lorenzo Valley High School, K. Gough; **170** Lincoln High School, Lori Green

Student Book Classroom Photography

3 Lincoln High School, Lori Green; **14** Lincoln High School, Lori Green; **27** Lincoln High School, Lori Green; **36** Lincoln High School, Lori Green; **42** San Lorenzo Valley High School, Kim Gough; **55** Lincoln High School, Lori Green; **95** Foothill High School, Sheryl Dozier; **104** Foothill High School, Sheryl Dozier; **114** Mendocino Community High School, Lynne Alper; **127** Mendocino High School, Lynne Alper; **150** Lake View High School, Carol Caref; **157** West High School, Janice Bussey; **189** Whitney Young High School, Carol Berland; **210** Pleasant Valley High School, Michael Christensen; **222** Lynne Alper; **238** East Bakersfield High School, Susan Lloyd; **252** Lincoln High School, Lynne Alper; **274** Colton High School, Sharon Taylor; **281** Foothill High School, Sheryl Dozier; **307** Santa Cruz High School, Lynne Alper; **324** Foothill High School, Cheryl Dozier; **352** Santa Maria High School, Mike Bryant; **366** Santa Cruz High School, Lynne Alper; **373** Shasta High School, Dave Robathan; **397** Santa Cruz High School, Lynne Alper; **414** Santa Maria High School, Mike Bryant; **424** Bartram Communications Academy, Robert Powlen; **446** Santa Maria High School, Mike Bryant; **460** Ranum High School, Rita Quintana

Front Cover Students

Katrina Van Loan, Jenee Desmond, David Trammell, Gina Uriarte, Thea Singleton, Itan Novis, Sarah N. Weintraub (photographed by Hilary Turner at Tamalpais High School)